THE HEALTHY ALTERNATIVE

D1286011

Also by John Houghton:

HAGBANE'S DOOM

The
Healthy
Alternative

JOHN HOUGHTON

KINGSWAY PUBLICATIONS
EASTBOURNE

ISBN 0 86065 345 5

Printed in Great Britain for
KINGSWAY PUBLICATIONS LTD
Lottbridge Drove, Eastbourne, E.Sussex BN23 6NT by
Cox & Wyman Ltd, Reading.
Typeset by Nuprint Services Ltd, Harpenden, Herts.

To
my dear wife, Janet, whose beautiful spirit
has been the greatest single human factor
in my own pilgrimage into wholeness

Contents

Introduction

Is man just a machine? Or is there, as Arthur Koestler said, 'A ghost in the machine'? Therein lies the current debate about human nature and conduct. Many scientists, behaviourists and sociologists have been content with the mechanistic approach. But that is being challenged afresh today by two groups of thinkers.

The one, I have dubbed the Aquarians; the other is the Christians. Neither is a unified whole, the former unavoidably, the latter regrettably; yet both share the common belief that man is more than a machine and needs to be treated as such. Both hold to the conviction that many of the ills of Western society must be attributed to a failure to recognize the true nature of man and of the universe in which he lives. They want to do something about it, to make us whole. They propose an alternative way of life.

Here the similarities end, for the world view of the Aquarians is fundamentally opposed to that of the Christians, though that is not always apparent because of their mutual claims to some form of spirituality. Part of my aim is to unmask that possible confusion.

I have not intended to present the Aquarian case in full—to do so would require far more substantial a book than this. I recently came across some fifty related titles on the subject in a small provincial bookstore! Nonetheless, I hope I have given enough idea of their position to do them some justice. The reader will also find comment on biorhythms, vegetarianism, transcendental meditation, yoga, primal scream therapy, massage, biofeedback, macrobiotics, radiesthesia, homeopathy and acupuncture.

My positive aim has been to present the case for Christian wholeness as the only healthy alternative. In this I am motivated by a three-fold conviction: the world is crying out for answers; Christians need to rise confidently to the challenge; most of us, myself included, have scarcely begun to appreciate the potential for life to be found in Jesus Christ.

To avoid being too academic about this at times complex subject, I have written the book as a small drama. I hope this will not only put flesh and bones upon the issues but also make it more readable to those who find that a storyline aids the digestion of facts.

In doing this I am aware of three dangers. The one is that of sacrificing form for content or *vice versa*.

The second is of making over-generalizations. The third is of erecting a 'straw man' in Mr Aquarius. I have done my best to handle these pitfalls, but how successfully, the reader must judge.

The structure of the drama is simple: the first two chapters analyse the problems; the second two look at the alternative remedies; the subsequent chapters consider the practical implications. I have drawn extensively upon my own experiences of people and have included some personal testimony. However, all the characters are fictitious (including the Pilgrim Watcher) though the issues discussed are very real. The appropriate venues are set in London as the place I know best.

One other comment concerns my own 'world-view'. The reader will encounter angels, good and bad, in the narrative and a word of explanation is called for. In accordance with the Bible, I hold to the existence of one, true, living, personal God and to the reality of the visible and invisible world he created. Within that cosmos is a divinely-permitted conflict which interacts in both spheres of existence. This long war is about truth, not simply the ideas of men but ultimate reality itself. From the beginning it has involved spirit-beings.

The coming in history of Jesus Christ, the Son of God, spelt a decisive defeat for the dark spiritual hosts, including their leader, Satan. The implementation of that victory is an ongoing process effected through the true church and one which will not be completed until Jesus returns to close off this age. This means that at times the conflict is with ideas which have satanic origin. Though we should not attribute all troubles to demons, on occasions we do deal directly with demonic opposition. Yet this is always against the backdrop of the victorious death and resurrection of Jesus Christ. Hence, in this battle the final triumph of truth and goodness is certain.

Finally, a book like this does not get written in isolation and I am grateful to many friends who have stimulated ideas and given prayerful encouragement. This has been especially true of the Christian community at South Lee, to which I am privileged to belong.

My particular thanks are due to Dr David Guckenheim MB, BS for checking the medical facts and making valuable amendments. Also to John Colwell BD for his perceptive comments on the theological and philosophical side. Neither is, of course, responsible for the final outcome.

My eldest daughter, Debbie, gave the manuscript a useful sixth-former's once-over. Janet, my wife, typed the first draft and half the final copy, and has been as superb a support as ever. Patricia Monk, my secretary, typed the other half. To both I am exceedingly grateful for their unstinting labours and patience.

Above all, my thanks to the Lord himself for his sustaining grace throughout the period of writing.

JOHN HOUGHTON

I have never before seen a man or a woman. I have lived all my life among shadows and broken images.

Ransom upon
meeting the King
and Queen of
Paradise in *Voyage
to Venus* by
C.S.Lewis.

Prologue

It was a late spring afternoon. The Courier stood on the lofty bridge spanning Archway Road, high above the roar of the ceaseless traffic. From this North London vantage point he gazed south across the steaming, misty mass of the city. Without moving, he waited until he heard the dull clunks of three car doors closing, then footsteps coming towards him. That one vehicle departed with an ascending swish did not in the least surprise him, nor did he turn to greet his expected guests, but still staring into the distance, he began instead to speak, a Welsh lilt betraying his origins.

'Western society is sick. It possesses the most advanced, the most sophisticated and affluent culture the world has ever seen; but it is sick. I feel the all-pervasive sense of disease; it hangs like a noxious cloud over the land.'

The slightly built Courier paused a moment, before continuing his mournful monologue. He wore a tatty brown suit which perfectly fitted his mood. Thirty years of life had etched their way into his lean melancholic face. The dark eyes of one who slept little and pondered often surveyed the scene.

'Crowded city streets full of lonely people; little children huddling their hurt selves into corners as their parents lust and scream their way to the divorce courts; hospitals and surgeries jam-packed with people suffering self-inflicted diseases. Stress, violence and anxiety like jagged rocks cut into the souls of millions, while others slowly drown in the grey swamps of apathy, cynicism and despair. Crime rates are soaring, industrial and political tension reigns, the Bomb threatens extinction for us all. How truly Isaiah the Prophet spoke, "The whole head is sick and the whole heart faint. From the sole of the foot even to the head there is no soundness in it."

'Gentlemen, is there any cure for this malicious malady? Or shall society merely continue to put its trust in tranquillizers and television to ease this self-inflicted torment? What is to be done as this once proud materialistic culture ekes out its remaining strength in cries of pain and distress?'

'*That* is what I have come to observe,' said the Pilgrim Watcher.

The Courier turned to address the tall, dark-cloaked figure who stood beside him. As in the past, he had received no more than a letter instructing him where to go, whom to meet and for what purpose. The letters never had an address but were simply signed with the symbol of a crowned lamb. The Courier never hesitated to obey.

'So, you arrived safely then? I hope you had a good journey. Can I ask where you've come from?'

'St Bartholomew's Day, 1662, to be precise,' replied the Pilgrim Watcher in a deep, strong voice. 'Which accounts for my present clothing.'

He was dressed in the traveller's fashion of that day with his long cloak, high boots and broad-rimmed hat. Only the suffused glow in his eyes betrayed his celestial origins. The clothing would not need changing, for few in this generation would be able to see him and those who could would understand.

'Ah, the Great Ejection. A dark day for England,' the Courier answered.

'Indeed. But fire driven underground may continue to

burn no less fiercely for all that; a fact which I have often witnessed in my travels. But time presses or I would tell you more. Who, pray, are our companions?'

Two men who were standing behind them were introduced by the Courier as Mr Aquarius and Mr Christian. The former was a casual framed man in his late thirties. He had an earnest face and a somewhat sallow complexion accentuated by the black polo necked sweater and cords he wore. His receding hair and beard matched his clothes. Mr Christian was of similar age and also bearded. He wore jeans and an open-necked red shirt. His eyes were lively and he possessed the ruddy complexion and build of one who was physically active. He did not look the religious type.

'And will either or both of you show me the answer to this awful problem which the Courier has—shall I say—raised for our consideration?' the Pilgrim Watcher asked.

'Raised for our consideration, yes, but this is no mere academic problem,' Mr Aquarius responded at once. 'I agree with what the Courier says; something is genuinely wrong with this society and it needs a radical answer. But I don't share his sense of gloom. I believe we stand upon the threshold of a new day of opportunity, a time to right these wrongs. My day, in fact.'

'And what is your day?' the Pilgrim Watcher enquired politely.

'It's a New Age; a day of power. Oh, I don't mean the political kind, but a release of the essential Life Force which pulsates through the universe,' he declared. 'This generation has ignored the psychic and spiritual dimensions of life. People have lived partial, fragmented lives. They are shut into a merely materialistic understanding of the world in which they live. No wonder they have such broken sickly lives. I come proclaiming a way to wholeness and health which will liberate mankind into a new dimension of living.'

'And what is the key to all this? How can we get your new way of living?' asked the Courier.

'Man must learn to awaken his spiritual nature and tune into the Force. Then he will come into harmony with his environment. The materialist is always in conflict with his world; he sees it as a threat to be conquered, and full of contradictions. My new man has learned, as it were, to flow with the tide, to rise and set with the sun, to soar on the wind. He *feels* oneness with the Force. He becomes a whole man.' Mr Aquarius was nothing if not enthusiastic.

'Do you have a special community or a place where you give instruction on this way?' the Pilgrim Watcher asked.

'Well, I live in a commune, as a matter of fact,' he replied. 'But really we're getting in everywhere. You'll find our beliefs in everything from yoga classes to yoghurt diets, from astral travel to acupuncture. We're even beginning to get scientists interested in our methods at long last, for we offer nothing less than a non-violent way of advancing the evolution of the human race.'

'A noble thought indeed,' acknowledged the Pilgrim Watcher. He turned to Mr Christian, noting the sparkle in his eyes and feeling the near kinship of one who worshipped the Lamb.

'As an outsider, I'd say that Christians have been through rather a lot in recent years,' put in the Courier. 'In fact, the way I look at it, they've suffered a major identity crisis which, to my mind, they've only just survived by the skin of their teeth. But times are changing, and they seem to be a lot more lively and sure of themselves these days.'

'Like the fire that burns underground,' murmured the Pilgrim Watcher. 'Well, Mr Christian, what do you have to say about the world today?'

'It's reaping what it has sown,' Mr Christian replied simply. 'For a long time now, Western man has believed in his own ability to solve all his problems. He's made education, science and technology his gods; he's made economic gain and personal freedom his goals. He believes he can go it alone.'

'So what are you trying to say?' Mr Aquarius interrupted.

'I'm saying that the mess we're in today is the result of this thinking,' he explained. 'In the 1960s people decided to "do their own thing" and reject the moral values of Christ's teaching. It was a tragic mistake. They planted a poisonous seed and now we reap its bitter fruits.'

'Couldn't you stop it when you saw it happening?' queried the Courier.

'I'm tempted to say we caused it,' Mr Christian replied with candour. 'The church had largely lost its way in a maze of legalism, intellectual debates and denominational in-fighting. We'd forgotten our mission and quenched the Holy Spirit. What strength remained was mostly invested in middle-class suburban conformity.' He laughed. 'Little wonder the radical leaders of society despised us. We, who should have been leading a revolution into a new age, looked more like stuck-in-the-mud reactionaries!'

'So tell us, what has changed?' said the Pilgrim Watcher. 'For I observe from your face that you are now far removed from such a woebegone state.'

'Well, many of us began to pray and repent of our sins; we confessed our need of God, and he began to pour out his Holy Spirit on us again.' Mr Christian grinned. 'It was as though Sleeping Beauty had received the kiss of life. We awoke and shook off our rags and began to clothe ourselves for a new day. We began to rediscover the wonder of true fellowship and worship together—we learnt to worship with a joy the first Christians must have known.'

'I was there once,' mused the Pilgrim Watcher. 'Certainly those were wonderful days. But I interrupt. Please continue.'

'Communities of people filled with the Holy Spirit,' enthused Mr Christian, as his eyes caught the setting sun. 'This is the answer to the present problems. The totality of Christ dwelling in the church by the Spirit is the one thing powerful enough to make people whole and change society for the better.'

'If you don't mind me saying so,' Mr Aquarius interjected, 'that sounds remarkably similar to what I'm teaching, except that you will insist on putting it in this wretchedly archaic religious language.'

'The difference is quite fundamental,' Mr Christian responded warmly. 'For you, the answer lies in oneness with an impersonal Force. I believe that people are made whole through oneness with the living God through Jesus Christ.'

'I can see we've got two contenders here!' cried the Courier. 'We're in for an interesting debate with you both claiming you know the secret of saving the world.'

The Pilgrim Watcher leaned on the bridge, looking out on the now darkening scene. Black, irregular clouds drifted across the misty pink of sunset. Lights winked like low white stars on the city skyscrapers. Sodium-lit streets stretched in all directions.

'Will they enter an age of mysticism, meditation and magic or will this be the era of the Spirit of Christ?' he mused aloud. 'Mr Aquarius seems confident but Mr Christian will have more to say than is expected. Nor will that be the first time. But of a truth, there is much work to be done.'

'By the way,' said the Courier, 'did you know that a lot of people have committed suicide from this bridge?'

'Then let us hasten to a safer place,' replied the Pilgrim Watcher, and turned away with a swirl of his cloak. The others agreed and, after making arrangements for the following day, they went off to their homes.

CHAPTER ONE

The Stress Factor

'I perceive that one need not be a bearded prophet of doom in order to find fault with this society,' said the Pilgrim Watcher. 'I have been listening to the people as they talk together and most of them seem to be heavy with sorrows and complaints.'

The Courier gave a thin-lipped smile. He didn't have a beard.

'They blame all sorts of things,' he replied. 'Those whose pockets are hardest hit echo the monotonous message of the media and successive governments and put it all down to the economy. Somebody waiting for an operation will blame the National Health Service. Others tell us it's all to do with food additives, pollution, nuclear power stations, lead in petrol and white flour.'

'Some of these things are strange to me,' the Pilgrim Watcher answered. 'But if those I have listened to already could see me I would tell them they are indeed a miserable lot! Seldom in my travels have I encountered a people more dissatisfied with their way of life, and yet with such opportunity to be happy. They have lost the ability to be thankful to their Creator.'

'If you ask me, it's all because people haven't got a positive moral and spiritual base to their lives,' interjected

Mr Christian, who had just joined them. 'Folk just don't have anything to build on today—except self-interest, of course. I was talking to a senior Youth Officer and he said, "I had a religious base to my childhood, but the kids today have no bottom line to their lives. There's nothing to stop them from sliding into the abyss. I'm worried for the future." '

'That's a far cry from a few years back,' said the Courier, 'when it was the done thing to cast off restraint, to "let it all hang out" and to indulge the appetites at will. Perhaps you're right, Mr Christian, when you say we reap what we sow. People reared on an amoral, self-centred philosophy of personal pleasure have become victims of their own indulgence.'

Mr Christian concurred with the Courier and said that this was the reason he felt a radical answer was needed which did not just treat the symptoms but cured the disease and created a healthy new way of life.

'I'm sure Mr Aquarius would say yes to that,' said the Courier. 'But where is the man? He's late today.'

The three were standing in the foyer of a large hotel, waiting for Mr Aquarius. The Courier's first instructions were to arrange for his party to consider the major problems of twentieth century culture so that Mr Aquarius and Mr Christian could present their answers to the Pilgrim Watcher in the light of these. He had planned, therefore, that they should start off by attending a lecture on the subject of stress.

Eventually, Mr Aquarius arrived, apologizing profusely for the delay which had been caused by a lightning strike on the Underground. It took some moments to explain to the Pilgrim Watcher that this did not mean what he had hitherto understood it to mean!

Together they entered the comfortable lounge, along with about forty others, and took their seats. The Pilgrim Watcher sat, invisible to most, on the side. He drew from his cloak a scroll, a quill pen and an inkhorn in readiness to take notes.

The lecturer was a lady, Dr Evans. She began in crisp tones.

'A person without any stress is dead. All living things require a degree of stress for the maintenance of life and health, be that the tension of the cell wall in an amoeba, the pressure of the rising spring sap in a sycamore tree or the rhythmic pumping of our own hearts. Indeed all our muscles, if they are healthy, retain a certain springiness or inbuilt tension which we call *tonus* and we can get some idea of a person's general health by measuring this.

'Now not only is healthy tension good for our bodies but, if we wish to improve our physique, we must actually increase the level of stress upon ourselves. We do this by means of exercises such as running, weight training or swimming. In fact, to make a really significant change in strength or suppleness the stress must reach the point of discomfort and mild pain.'

Mr Christian whispered to the Courier, 'My old gym instructor used to say that. He'd have us hanging like wet rags from the wall bars trying to lift our legs to right angles. "Keep at it chaps," he'd shout. "It's the one that hurts that does you good!" '

'The trouble is, it's true,' smiled the Courier.

A cough and a pointed look from the Doctor brought them back. She continued, 'What we find to be true in the physical realm is also the case in the psychological. Without a degree of stress upon our minds and emotions, both from within and without, we would quickly degenerate to a mere vegetable existence.

'Artists, for example, acknowledge that their creations spring forth from some inner drive, even a passionate compulsion, which must find expression in paint, music, words or whatever. If it were not for these drives mountains might never be climbed, mysteries of science would remain unsolved and humankind would still be crouching in caves.

'Good relationships, too, include healthy stresses. My

best friends are prepared *not* to agree with everything I say and it's the cut and thrust of our friendly debates over a pint or a meal which stimulates our minds, enlarges our self-understanding and deepens our mutual appreciation—even when our views differ absolutely!

'We see the same thing in that deepest of human commitments, marriage. Partners who possess quite opposite characteristics and who, therefore, approach life from differing perspectives, seem to have the most successful marriages. Perhaps one of the joys of developing love is learning how to agree about what colour the curtains should be, after you have at first totally disagreed. Far from destroying a relationship this kind of tension enhances it.'

The Pilgrim Watcher thought Dr Evans was probably happily married.

'Finally, children themselves grow by being carefully stretched and encouraged in their abilities. Nature has so designed things that hunger pains motivate babies to cry for food. Later on, we teach children to walk and later still prepare them for exams or sports competitions. To do these things correctly and to avoid the extremes of either neglect or excessive pressure is the art of good child-rearing.

'These, then, are examples of natural, healthy stresses which are essential to life and well being.'

A few questions were asked at this point, after which Dr Evans announced a five minute break.

*   *   *

The coffee, which Mr Aquarius declined to drink, was as unpalatable as any served up at this kind of function and they were quite glad to get back to their seats ready for the next session. Dr Evans began once more.

'When most people think of stress today they usually mean something *un*healthy. "Uptight", "neurotic" and "screwed up" are typical descriptions of those suffering from an excess of tension. That more and more are suffering in this way is our major concern.

'Now in order to grasp the significance of bad stress on the personality I am going to draw a comparison with a length of piano wire under tension.'

She projected a transparency on the screen thus:

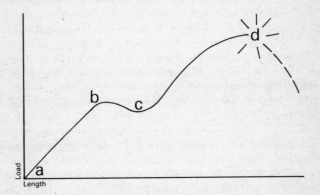

'I won't bore you with the technical details but the points to note are as follows:

'Healthy stress lies between points *a* and *b*. Within these limits the stretched wire will return to its normal length as soon as the load is removed.

'However, increase the load too much and somewhere between points *b* and *c* the wire will remain permanently stretched when the pull is removed. It will have lost its resilience and will never be the same again without some radical treatment such as melting it down and refashioning it. This is what the dangerous condition of overstress is like and it is the unfortunate state of many in our modern world.

'Increase the load only slightly on this now brittle wire and it will rapidly reach point *d*—breaking point. The wire will snap. This is what constitutes a nervous breakdown; a person living under excessive stress reaches the point where he can no longer cope, so he "cracks up".'

Dr Evans then proposed three factors which related to overstress. They were personality, environment and conscience. She began by contrasting what she described as *Type A* and *Type B* personalities.

'Bill leaps out of bed in the morning, grabs his digital watch and worries that he's already twenty-five seconds behind schedule. He wrenches the cap from off the tooth-paste tube, curses when he drops it in the bathtub, grabs at it impatiently and stuffs it back on the tube only to realize he has forgotten to put any paste on his brush. After washing, he charges into the bedroom and rummages through the wardrobe to find the shirt he wants—which, of course, is in the washing. After berating his poor wife he thunders downstairs to bolt down a slice of toast and a cup of strong coffee, all the time watching the clock. At precisely seven-thirty Bill grabs his briefcase, rushes from the house and into the car.

'Once behind the steering wheel, he really winds up. He stabs the key into the ignition and tries to start the car. "Come on, come on," he mutters through gritted teeth as the much maligned motor refuses to start. When it does eventually splutter into life, he rockets down the drive and hurtles as fast as he can to the nearest traffic jam. There he fumes, tapping the wheel, revving the engine, glancing at the dash clock, putting the car in and out of gear. And so it goes on. Bill has started his day. He is a *Type A* personality, always in a hurry and full of impatience.

'Unless Bill can change his approach to life he is heading for at least an ulcer and a heart attack. He is unlikely to enjoy life in the middle years or to survive the shock of retirement.

'Mary, on the other hand, is quite different. She begins her day calmly with a luxurious stretch, wanders through her early morning ritual, takes time out to smile at the house plants and has to remind herself even of the existence of clocks. She is not so well organized as Bill but then is not so frustrated when things go wrong. Traffic jams don't worry her unduly; they give her more time to enjoy the D.J.'s badinage on the morning radio or to preen her face in the powder-compact mirror. If she's a bit late for work, it's not her fault. "The traffic was bad," she smiles sweetly.

'Does Mary have any problems? She may well put on weight as the years pass because her metabolism is slower than Bill's. Her lack of drive will limit her prospects and may well frustrate her more zealous companions. But she is very unlikely to suffer the major stress diseases to which Bill is prone. She is a *Type B* personality.'

Dr Evans paused for a question from the floor.

'But surely you are polarizing the extremes, Doctor? Most of us are neither one nor the other.'

'That is correct,' she replied. 'The majority are a mixture of the two types. I deliberately overstated their characteristics to make the point. But, nonetheless, I come across far too many "Bill's" in my surgery for comfort. I would just say that if you recognize yourself in the *Type A* category, beware!'

The Doctor proceeded to tackle what she considered to be the unique environmental stress factors of the twentieth century.

'The first is to do with the sheer pace of life, which has increased dramatically over the past century. Let me illustrate what I mean. Did you know that until 1600 BC the fastest form of transport was the camel caravan averaging eight m.p.h.? This was eclipsed at that time by a new means of travel which sped along at the phenomenal rate of twenty m.p.h. It was the horse drawn chariot. So successful was the chariot that nothing went faster until 1880, when the steam locomotive improved on its original thirteen m.p.h. to reach a hundred m.p.h. Since that time, of course, man-kind has gone ever faster and can now orbit the earth at 18,000 m.p.h. Few of us attain those speeds but the majority think nothing of travelling at seventy m.p.h. on the roads and faster on inter-city trains.

'The effects are interesting. At the physical level, especially for drivers, we find speed creates a stress situation. Both blood pressure and pulse rate rise and the adrenal glands increase their output as the body seeks to cope with the natural fear which is generated. However, the driver cannot run away and thereby dissipate this reaction, as our forebears could. He is stuck in his seat, and this makes for an unhealthy situation.

'At the psychological level, increased speed tends to create a *desire* for speed. In other words, it is addictive. This may be due partly to the "high" created by the release of adrenalin. But there are other factors too. The faster we travel, the more information we have to assimilate through our eyes and we become used to this high level of mental activity, so that life can appear frustrating when we slow down. Witness how hard it is to drive at thirty miles an hour after leaving a motorway.

'There is no doubt that the increased pace has, without their realizing it, led people to expect things to happen rapidly; it's given them the desire to do things more quickly "in order to save time". Nobody knows what the time is being saved for; all too often it is just to do other things faster in order to save time... ad infinitum.

'I have a friend called Roger. Recently, he expressed his frustration with the dial on the telephone because of the time it took to make a call. He wants to get a push button system instead. Out of interest, I did an experiment and found it took me only fifteen seconds to dial the longest seven figure number, 000 0000. It takes three seconds to press out 123 4567. Why does Roger want to save a mere twelve seconds, except that somehow the pace of life has got to him? He is suffering from what I call residual speed stress.'

Doctor Evans' second environmental factor was what she called communication saturation. She observed that never before has a society been bombarded with so much information, be it through advertising, newscasts or the endless chatter of radio and television.

'Of course, we have ways of coping with all this by selectively shutting out a large proportion of what we see and hear. Advertisers recognize this phenomenon and are continually bending their resources to regain our attention. Newsmen, likewise, are aware of it—hence the need to continually dramatize the news, particularly on television. Yet, even though we can ignore much of the information which comes our way, we are still left with a vast amount which demands decisions and emotional responses from us—and this is a stress factor, especially for susceptible individuals.

'Sally is a middle-aged mum already going through a trying time. She decided to become more socially aware and so gave herself to absorbing as much news and social comment as possible. The result? Despair, fear and depression. And this for the simple reason that the very activity of considering the threatening information, which in reality could not affect her personally, demanded too much of her. Her stress level, therefore, reached danger point.'

'Men fainting with fear and with foreboding of what is coming on the world.'[1] murmured Mr Christian.

'What was that?' asked Doctor Evans, overhearing.

'Oh sorry, just some words of Jesus I recalled,' replied Mr Christian a little embarrassed. He repeated them.

'Very apt comment, I'm sure,' she responded drily and proceeded to the other environmental stress factor peculiar to modern society. She described this as the *rate* of change brought about by the technological revolution.

'I am not yet forty years of age.' She smiled challengingly, for she was not far off it. 'When I was a little girl my mother used an old-fashioned scrubbing board every Monday morning to do the washing. I turned the mangle and she pegged the wet clothes on the line, hoping for fine weather. By the time I married we had a twin tub. Ten years ago my

[1] Luke 21:26

husband and I bought an automatic; five years later we added a tumble drier and next year we shall purchase an electronic model to combine both operations.

'It's only a matter of time before the linen basket is replaced by an automatic sorting device which grades and washes fabrics every time there is a sufficient quantity and returns them ready-to-wear. The scrubbing board technology is thousands of years old; in under half a century we have progressed to the place where "doing the washing" is virtually a thing of the past.

'This rate of change, this acceleration produced by self-fuelling technology, affects every area of our lives. But it requires tremendous and continuous adjustments on our part just to avoid being left behind. For many it is simply too much and they begin to show stress symptoms as a result. This is what Alvin Toffler defined as "future shock", the inability to cope adequately with too rapid a rate of change.'

Dr Evans waited a few moments to allow the class to catch up with their notes. Then she continued: 'The last cause of bad stress in society is a largely neglected one but significant for all that. I refer to the tension caused by bad conscience or personal guilt.'

Mr Christian brightened visibly at this point.

'Anthea's marriage had been a so-called "bouquet of barbed wire" and broke up after sixteen years. It was the usual sad story of "the other woman". She had found out and confronted her husband with the facts, which he had acknowledged. She tried to forgive him but, in the end, found what she thought would be comfort—though it was probably revenge—in a willing boyfriend. Her husband discovered this and was typically outraged at her lack of fidelity! End of marriage, separation and divorce.

'It was not just the loneliness nor having to cope with all the family responsibilites which drove Anthea to tran-quillizers. It was lying in bed at night feeling the awful guilt and failure of her life. Where had she gone wrong? She had failed. Her broken marriage vows haunted her. Her hatred and bitterness towards her ex-husband both frightened and appalled her. What did her children think of her now? She saw their hurt lives, their suspicious eyes, their withdrawn moods and increasingly violent outbursts. Oh God, what had she done? God…yes, rightly or wrongly, she believed in God. What did he think of her?

'Anthea is one of my case histories and her story is repeated thousands of times over. But there are other guilty secrets which cause inner distress and bring people to our surgeries. The petty crime, the evil deed, the cruel action which cannot now be remedied. Whether we like it or not, we remain stubbornly moral creatures and, unless we can find a better resolution to the problems this raises than we have at present, we shall continue to spend vast sums on psychiatric care.'

By now Mr Christian was fairly bursting to comment but Dr Evans had her eye on the clock and continued rapidly.

'I want to sum up what I have said this morning. Stress has a healthy value, up to a certain point; exceed that and we have problems, either of residual overstress or nervous breakdown. Unhealthy stress is brought about by temperamental susceptibility, by various environmental factors unique to this generation and by personal guilt feelings.

'Any serious attempt at reducing the level of stress in our lives will have to tackle these three areas. It will need to be an eminently constructive, active therapy which will adjust our personalities where necessary, relieve the environmental factors and provide an effective treatment for both real and imagined guilt. After lunch we shall break into small discussion groups to consider whether or not our present approaches to the problem are adequate . Thank you for your attention. We'll take the break now.'

With that the class adjourned for lunch.

*   *   *

It so happened that the four men were able to be in the same group after lunch along with a Mr and Mrs Grimsdyke, both middle-aged, he overweight, she highly strung and still wearing her overcoat. They were there for her 'nerves'. The other member of the group introduced herself as Penny, a young doctor's receptionist. The Pilgrim Watcher remained invisible to all but his three companions, so had to keep silent.

'It seems to me,' ventured Mr Aquarius, 'that the main problem with our approach to stress is that it's essentially passive. Instead of dealing with the root issues we merely use some form of tranquillizer. And the most popular seem to me to be cigarettes and alcohol.'

'George smokes, don't you George?' Mrs Grimsdyke piped up.

'So would you, woman, if you had to put up with what I have to,' George mumbled in reply. He looked at his yellowed fingers. 'Been smoking ever since I were a lad, though. Wish I could give it up sometimes but I can't.'

'A lot of people find that,' Penny chimed in. 'In fact nicotine is so addictive that many heroin addicts find it harder to kick than "mainlining".'

'There you are, George. You're worse than a drug addict,' said Mrs Grimsdyke. 'Perhaps that's why my nerves are so bad. I'm living with an addict!'

'But why do people smoke in the first place?' asked the Courier.

'I think it's often to act big; to appear grown up,' offered Mr. Christian. 'But more to the point is, why do they continue?'

Mr Aquarius felt it was because nicotine is a depressant drug which, after its initial kick, sedates the central nervous system. It makes the smoker feel relaxed but it is not true relaxation. Though the mind is muffled from reality, nicotine acts as a stimulant on the body. It artificially raises the metabolism, blood pressure goes up and adrenalin is released which, because it is not worked off, remains at unacceptably high levels.

Penny nodded. 'To say nothing of lowered vitality, hypertension, strokes, bronchitis and lung cancer. Did you know that you have seven times more chance of contracting lung cancer than a non-smoker, Mr Grimsdyke?'

'George, you can stop smoking at once!' his wife shrieked.

George Grimsdyke sighed and changed the subject.

'Now what about booze?' he said. 'We probably all drink. But if we're going to cut the pleasures out of life, we might as well go on the wagon. No half measures now. If we're going to be miserable, let's do it thoroughly!'

'Well, at least wine and beer have some food value,' the Courier said, a trifle defensively, for he liked his pint. 'In fact, at least some doctors consider it does more good to drink moderately than not at all because of the overall benefits, which include relaxation.'

'You Christians don't imbibe at all, do you?' Mr Aquarius asked of Mr Christian.

'Well, some don't, but many of us these days feel happy with drinking in moderation,' he replied.

'Ah, but what's moderation, m'lad, that's what I want to know?' Mr Grimsdyke demanded.

'I think it's to do with drinking for the right reasons,' Mr Christian suggested. 'When people drink to drown their sorrows or, more to the point of our discussion, to reduce the pressure they feel, then something's wrong . People who *need* alcohol to sustain their lifestyle are almost certainly addicted, even if they never actually get drunk.'

'I agree,' said Penny. 'But one of the problems today is that it's so easy to buy liquor in the supermarket and we're seeing a growing number of housewives who have become "respectable" alcoholics as a result. People who are bored, lonely and depressed are very vulnerable, so I'm not sure whether it isn't best to abstain altogether rather than run the risk.'

'You're saying then that alcoholism arises as a result of other things that are wrong in a person's lifestyle?' Mr

Aquarius asked.

She nodded.

'That's what I feel,' he continued. 'People misuse alcohol as a tranquilliser because they lack a balanced, wholesome lifestyle. And *that's* what I want to talk about.'

'And so you shall,' the Courier assured him. 'But not today, if you don't mind. Now I think we've spent enough time on the effects of alcohol and I'd like us to talk about another sedative which is in widespread use.'

They agreed but not until they had noted the heavy drinker's diseases of cirrhosis, heart and kidney troubles, as well as 'beer gut'. Not to mention appalling road casualties resulting from drunken driving.

'What's your sedative then, Mr Courier?' asked Mrs Grimsdyke, who had sat in a certain embarrassed silence during the discussion on alcohol.

'Television,' he replied. 'The flickering screen that seduces us into a fantasy world of soap operas, racy adventures, fickle quiz shows and superficial documentaries; all designed to detach us from reality.'

'But I like Coronation Street and Dallas,' Mrs Grimsdyke protested. 'I don't see that it's harmful if people want to enjoy themselves. It's up to them.'

'I feel it's harmful to watch television too much,' said Mr Christian. 'Living in this kind of fantasy world produces a terrible apathy and indifference to what's going on around us. I support those who want to clean up television and I believe that the portrayal of sex and violence does lead some susceptible people to go out and do such things themselves. But I also feel that the real problem is that the majority of people can watch even the most horrific things and remain completely unmoved. And even if they are disturbed, there's always the next programme or another channel.'

'It's another passive means of coping with stress and like the others it's got undesirable side effects,' said the Courier. 'The one that concerns me is the way television destroys communication. People don't talk about their problems or even just chat because a particular programme is on. Kids get bored with what their parents are watching so they roam the streets and land up in trouble. They don't talk about how they got on at school because the box is on from the moment they arrive home. I mean, some programmes are good. They can be quite creative and stimulating—but nobody thinks of responding. They just sit there. They're being taught alienation.'

'George never talks to me in an evening, do you, George?' said Mrs Grimsdyke. 'He goes to sleep in front of the telly half the time. Don't know why he watches it.'

'It's the only relaxation I get, woman. Anyway, I couldn't put up with an evening of your nagging, could I?'

The Courier coughed. 'Well then, most of us are agreed that people watch television as a way of coping with stress. It's a powerful drug, and big business knows it. Look at the vast sums of money spent on it, let alone all the new investments in video and cable television to give us an even greater choice of fantasy for longer times, so that we don't have to cope with the real world.'

'Can I raise another topic?' Penny requested. 'I reckon that nearly half the prescriptions I give out on behalf of my boss are for tranquillizers of one kind or another, mostly to people who aren't undergoing any particular crisis but just can't cope with life itself.'

'Why does he do it?' asked the Courier.

Penny said she thought it was simply because he was so busy. People came to him as though he were a high priest who had a solution to all their problems. Not having all the answers but knowing that people expected something from him, he gave them some tablets to get them over the difficult period. The trouble was, many of his patients came back for repeat prescriptions for years on end and became addicts.

'That's an awful state to be in,' Mr Aquarius said. 'But I think the reason for so many tablets being prescribed goes deeper. The Western concept of man is wholly materialistic and so he thinks of himself as nothing more than a sophisticated electro-chemical machine. When things go wrong he puts himself in for a service. If he's not running too well he looks for a chemical solution as the easiest way of putting matters right.'

Mr Christian took up the theme. 'But sedatives don't solve problems,' he said. 'They only appear to. If it was generally true that accidental chemical imbalances caused stress and depression then they might be an appropriate remedy; but I think what Dr Evans was teaching us this morning points in another direction. Stress is caused by a bad lifestyle and a wrong approach to living. Now it may well show up as a chemical imbalance which a chemical sedative will be able to correct...'

'Well, what's wrong with that?' interrupted Mr Grimsdyke.

'Tranquillizers appear successful on the surface,' he replied. 'But all that really happens is that the painful experience is repressed.' He paused and stroked his beard for a moment. 'Think about sleep. Most of us have times when we experience insomnia, and stress of one kind or another is usually the cause. Maybe we've an unresolved problem or our minds are just catching up with the filing, as it were. Give us time, and perhaps a friend to talk things over with, and we resume a normal sleep pattern, which includes dream release. This is our healthy way of handling life's pressures.

'But if you start taking sleeping tablets, although the immediate effect is "a good night's sleep", the problems aren't thought through and the dream mechanism is blocked. If problems don't get released they become repressed and in the long run that may cause some kind of neurosis or insidious damage to the body.'

'My tablets make me constipated,' said Mrs Grimsdyke.

'Yes, and they probably also destroy some of your vitamin stores and generally lower your health and vitality,' said Penny. 'In fact, after a few weeks a lot of our patients feel no benefit from taking the popular tranquillizers and many feel that they're trapped in a kind of "cotton wool world". The trouble is, Mrs Grimsdyke, you're probably addicted to a useless drug which is only lowering the quality of life and not solving your real problems at all.'

Penny was a gentle person and Mrs Grimsdyke, sensing someone understanding, promptly burst into tears. Mr Grimsdyke shuffled away 'to get some fresh air' and the others discreetly left Penny and the distraught woman together. The Pilgrim Watcher thought Penny could dimly see him so he smiled encouragingly and fancied that she responded.

*   *   *

The four companions stood opposite the entrance to Sloane Square underground station watching people coming and going.

'Their faces look sad and drawn,' observed the Pilgrim Watcher. 'It is as the Strategic Council thought. My report will only confirm their fears.'

'All the answers people turn to are passive; that's clear enough,' the Courier said. 'They're no real answer to the mess we're in. It is high time somebody came up with a more wholesome remedy.'

'Amen,' said Mr Christian.

'Yes,' Mr Aquarius assented.

At that moment, there was a squeal of brakes and the dull crunch of metal as two cars collided. The drivers leapt out and confronted each other angrily. Shouting and swearing filled the air. Onlookers gathered with a slight sparkle of interest on their otherwise dull faces.

Mr Grimsdyke dragged his sobbing wife through the crowd to the station entrance.

'You stupid woman, Ethel. Why didn't you look where you were going? Come on, down here before we get the blame for it.'

They disappeared into the Underground. The Courier sighed and said, 'Breaking point, gentlemen, when stress explodes into violence. That's enough for today, I think; tomorrow we'll look at the other big sickness of this society. Goodnight to you now.'

CHAPTER TWO

The Belly God

'I once heard the philosopher Epicurus say, "The beginning and the root of all good is the pleasure of the stomach; even wisdom and culture must be referred to this." I perceive your society has been reared upon this notion.'

The Pilgrim Watcher made his observation after walking round the supermarkets in a Lewisham shopping precinct, where he had been amazed not only by the vast quantity and variety of food available but by the way people jostled and grabbed for it, as though it was all going to vanish at any moment.

The four men sat on the grass outside the Hare and Billet on Blackheath Common, a tranquil, green oasis rising defiantly above the grubby urban wastelands below. The sun shone and even the distant roar of the A2 traffic was muted in the sweet haze which hung shimmering over the grassland. Birds chirruped happily in the trees surrounding the still pond outside the pub. The buzz of conversation and occasional laughter from other small groups of lunchtime drinkers made even the Courier smile into his beer.

'Didn't your apostle Paul say something like that?' he asked Mr Christian.

'Yes, but he wrote with considerable sadness about people whose god is the belly,' Mr Christain replied.

'Whose god is the belly. The belly god.'

The Courier rolled the phrase around his Welsh tongue a few times, staring thoughtfully into the distance.

'Look now,' he said suddenly, 'I want us to talk about this. There's a recent report by the Royal College of Physicians. They reckon that one third of all Britons are overweight for the simple reasons that we eat too much and don't do enough exercise. And they say the problem worsens with age; whereas, let me see, only 5% of children are overweight, by the mid-twenties it's risen to one third and by middle age fully 50% of the population are carrying too much fat. What do you think of that?'

The report to which he was referring showed that overweight people face quite serious health risks especially as they grow older. These include high blood pressure, gout, breathlessness, heart disease, maturity-onset diabetes, bowel and prostate cancers, varicose veins and osteoarthritis. Not only that, but overall life expectancy is reduced into the bargain.

'The psychological and social implications of obesity are no less worrying,' the Courier went on. 'The "happy fatty" really is a bit of a myth; even naturally cheerful people with a weight problem often nurse secret sorrows over their condition, and many others, especially women, are plainly depressed. They see themselves as people who are useless, just because they're overweight. It's even worse when they can't attract the opposite sex, and it's the last straw when fashion houses don't design clothes for fat people. Many overweight men, in particular, find their problem stops them taking part in sports and that means they miss out on the social friendship that you get with sports clubs.

'I read recently that an employer sacked a girl because she was overweight. He said she couldn't be expected to have either the health record or the performance-capability of a slim person. I wonder if that will become a trend?'

'I don't know,' answered Mr Aquarius. 'But it does suggest that people are beginning to take the problem seriously. Quite a lot of research has been going on in recent years and a number of "theories of fat" have been put forward. I must say, though, that most of them don't impress me very much because they miss the real problem.'

'You mean theories about heredity factors, like body types and metabolic rates?' asked Mr Christian.

The Pilgrim Watcher, who had neither inherited his body nor ever given a thought as to why the Strategic Council had given him one which was tall and lean, was quite mystified by all this. He didn't even have a metabolic rate, as far as he knew.

The others explained that physiologists make a distinction between three types of physical build: endomorphs who tend to be rounded, mesomorphs who are muscular and ectomorphs who are wiry. No one can change the body type with which they are born, but that does not mean an overweight endomorph, say, can do nothing about it. There are plenty of successful sports men and women of all body types to prove otherwise. And metabolic rate can be significantly affected by exercise.

Out came the Pilgrim Watcher's writing implements and he began to pen fast and furiously.

'The trouble with paying too much attention to weight theories,' Mr Christian expostulated, 'is that they encourage passivity. People blame their problems on their hormones when, in fact, the vast majority who are overweight are that way simply because they're over indulgent.'

Mr Aquarius looked askance and the Courier blinked. Mr Christian gave an apologetic smile. 'Sorry, I didn't mean just to criticize those whose sins show on their waistline; I believe it's a problem affecting the whole of Western society. We're an over indulgent race, and I think it's all to do with this "belly god". Unless we deal with *that* we'll have the obese struggling all their lives to lose weight and having to add the word "failure" to their list of troubles, whilst the slimmer ones will live in proud complacency and not realize that they can be just as self-indulgent, not only with food but with other things as well.'

Mr Aquarius felt Mr Christian had better explain what he meant by this. The latter gladly agreed.

'I believe we've a basic philosophy which is one of self-gratification or, if you like, "the right to indulge". It became popular with the rise of the permissive society and catch phrases like, "Do your own thing", "Whatever turns you on", or "Let it all hang out". It was a rejection of self-discipline and responsibility in favour of indulging our desires at will. It all boils down to feeding our personal greed—serving the belly god. So over eating is really only one side of a bigger problem.

'There are, of course, plenty who'll exploit this "right to indulge" mentality,' he continued. 'The adverts put out by the food industry cleverly encourage us to feed our greed, be it by challenging us to eat three helpings where popular sports personalities can manage only two, or by offering us the tantalizing seductiveness of sizzling pork sausages, or the sensuous thrill that they say comes with eating a bar of chocolate.'

Mr Aquarius came in, 'I'll at least agree with your last point. Food processing companies have learned the art of stimulating our appetites even further by the use of chemical additives, colourants and sugars, so that anybody who lives to a significant degree on processed foods will tend to eat more than is good for them.'

'Please explain yourself, Mr Aquarius,' said the Pilgrim Watcher.

'Well, whereas fresh, natural foods satisfy normal appetite in reasonable quantities, processed foods tend to artificially stimulate the appetite beyond the body's requirements so that people eat more than is good for them. Which is fine for the food company's profits, but not for the waistline.'

'So you wouldn't recommend processed foods?' the Courier asked.

'That's right, but not just for that reason. I believe, too, that eating whole foods is one of the ways of producing whole people. All these additives not only harm the body but affect the personality as well. My wife and I won't touch that kind of stuff at all and I believe we're better for it. Get people on to a natural diet and they'll not only be physically healthier but they'll be better adjusted people as well.'

Mr Christian felt strongly that this was missing the whole point and said so in no uncertain terms. Although he saw plenty of good reasons for eating whole foods he felt they had no moral or spiritual value whatsoever.

Seeing the two bearded men beginning to bristle, the Courier laughed.

'Okay, boyos. I'll get our glasses refilled if you don't mind. But then we must be on our way. Go and look at the pond, before you give yourselves indigestion!'

Twenty minutes later they left their pleasant watering place to visit a slimming club in a run-down Methodist Hall.

*   *   *

The club was fairly typical of its kind and consisted of about twenty people, mostly women, of various shapes and sizes, who were sitting in a semi-circle. The class was led by a smartly dressed woman of the medium build that would give us all hope. She later introduced herself as Miranda. The session commenced with a pep-talk from her which was followed by some animated discussion. It was immediately apparent to the onlookers that losing weight was only one of the reasons these people were together. A good few of them just needed the opportunity to talk about the problems they were experiencing. Miranda later explained that this was all part of the social service her class provided.

Following on from the discussion, one or two recipes were shared and then the scales were brought forth, to a mixture of groans and apprehensive murmurings. Weigh-ins were accompanied by handclaps or mild rebukes.

When the session was over the four companions sat down with Miranda over a cup of tea.

'We've been discussing the problems of overweight,' the Courier began. 'My companion, Mr Christian, feels that it's part of a broader problem of over indulgence and I must confess I am inclined to agree with him. My other friend here, Mr Aquarius, feels that much of the problem stems from the kind of diet we eat. What do you think?'

Miranda answered carefully. 'I'm sure they both have a point really. People do overeat for a variety of reasons, and when they do it's usually harmful foods such as sweets and biscuits that they consume. In many cases the problem goes back to childhood. Think of the parent who spoils her child by giving him all she never had herself as a youngster. Or the number of children who, whenever they hurt themselves, are given a sweet or a biscuit "to make you feel better". That's often the origin of so-called comfort eating. Children reared in this way turn to sweet foods for consolation when they are feeling hurt, lonely or depressed.'

'They are unwise parents who teach their offspring that food is the means to happiness,' thought the Pilgrim Watcher.

The conversation passed on to the reasons why people want to lose weight. Miranda felt that health factors are very low on the list. She had the occasional businessman who had been warned by his doctor to shed some pounds, but that was all. She didn't know of anyone dieting for religious reasons. Most, especially the women who made up the larger part of her classes, had other motives for slimming. She continued:

'I would say women are under more pressure to be slim than men. The media continually propagate the view that the secret of happiness lies in having an ideal model girl figure, and many believe it. We have some sad cases, too, of women who believe their husbands will love them if only they lose the inches. That makes me angry,' she confessed. 'A woman should be loved for who she is not for her shape.'

'That's a vicious circle anyway, isn't it?' Mr Christian said. 'The woman who feels unloved in the first place is likely to eat for comfort and become obese, which may well give her husband problems, which she will sense and so eat yet more for comfort.'

'Sadly, that's true of some,' Miranda agreed. 'But, just to set the record straight, I should add that there are many women who just want to lose weight out of self-respect. They want to look slim because then they believe they are attractive; they want to wear clothes which don't make them look like sacks tied up round the middle; they want to have a body which will serve an attractive, lively personality. Very often their weight problem has simply arisen out of a combination of child-bearing, bad eating habits and lack of exercise. These are our most successful slimmers.'

Mr Christian noted the point for later.

They spent a good while together discussing various diets with their merits and demerits. Miranda felt there were many fad diets on the market and writers were cashing in on a fashionable trend. As far as she was concerned, weight loss took place if you ate fewer calories and did more exercise. A long term reform of eating habits gave permanent and relatively painless weight loss. She felt that the fad diets were trying to help those who could not do this but she repeated the point that some people have underlying problems which no diet in itself is going to solve.

'What do you think of low calorie diet aids?' asked Mr Aquarius.

'They're of very limited value,' she replied. 'They are, of course, expensive and sometimes I feel the customer is being ripped off. For example, there's one pricey margarine for slimmers which has half the calories of the ordinary stuff simply because the manufacturers have emulsified in 50% water. By rights it should be half price! You can do just as well by using half the amount of ordinary margarine and spraying your bread with water if you want it more moist! And many low-cal foods are made so appetizing that the dieter becomes a diet-aid guzzler. They hinder rather than help reform eating habits.'

'I recently read somewhere that 90% of dieters don't manage to keep their weight loss,' said the Courier. 'Is that true?'

Miranda blushed slightly, then laughed.

'You'll have me out of a job. But yes, I'm afraid so. There are lots of reasons, I suppose, but in the end they all come down to lack of sufficient motivation.'

'In other words the root issues remain,' said Mr Christian.

'I guess you have your point,' she smiled at him.

Shortly after, the company took their leave of Miranda, thanking her for giving them the time. They agreed to meet in town later on.

*   *   *

They were sitting in Trafalgar Square that evening after having taken a brief but distasteful walk through the sordid streets of Soho at the Courier's suggestion. The Pilgrim Watcher was in a sombre mood.

'I see an evil aspect of the belly god again,' he said at last. 'This is not the worship of sex—I have seen that in other places—but of godless indulgence of the appetites. The Enemy has a stronghold in that place.'

'That's what I want us to realize,' Mr Christian spoke earnestly. 'Our society is all the time concerned about symptoms but ignores the causes. We try to tackle, say, obesity but without the least concern over self-indulgence. In fact, I reckon the whole slimming trend itself is motivated by self-indulgence because it only denies the flesh for other fleshly benefits, like being admired, being loved, being freer to indulge other appetites, and so on. What we've seen tonight is another aspect of the same thing. Only this time it's sexual self-indulgence.'

'You Christians always have been anti-sex, haven't you?' challenged Mr Aquarius.

'Not at all,' replied Mr Christian warmly. 'I'm not denying that there have been some perversions of Christianity which have denied sexual pleasure but that's certainly not what the Bible teaches. Those of us who believe the Scriptures give a very important place to the enjoyment of sexual love—but within its God-given bounds of married fidelity.

'The trouble with this society is that it's taken sexual intercourse out of the realm of loving commitment and thrust it into that of self-gratification. Its sexual activities all become variant forms of masturbation. I don't think it's without significance that sexual desire is treated in the same way as hunger. If the latter can be satisfied on demand, why not the former with any willing partner or available source?'

The Courier said he felt that the outright rejection of traditional sexual values had taken place in the 1960s. In that decade society went on a sexual spree; virginity became a kind of personal complaint akin to acne; marital fidelity was despised as old-fashioned and unimaginative; pornography and perversion were made respectable.

'And the knock-on effects of this have been devastating,' he said. 'There's venereal diseases, particularly the newer ones like herpes, chlamydia, salpingitis and AIDS. They're at epidemic proportions. Then there's the link between promiscuity and cervical cancer. They all cost a fortune to treat, and cause who knows what wretchedness to the victims.

'Immorality is what it's all about. That's what got easy contraception for unmarried people. But nobody knows yet the long term effects of the Pill. What's it going to do to the fertility of future generations, I want to know, particularly when girls have been using it regularly from an early age? People are getting worried.

'And in spite of easy contraception, lots of women still become pregnant by accident and want a way out. Since the 1967 Abortion Act there've been about two million abortions in Great Britain. It must be the biggest act of infanticide in British history. Most of these were performed under "ground two" of the Act: "Risk of injury to mental or physical health of woman". To my mind, it's all highly suspect. One report has said that in most of these cases there's no real risk at all.'[1]

The Courier went on to draw attention to the under published physical and psychological effects on aborting mothers. A significant percentage are left with permanent physical damage as well as with many psychiatric problems, including serious suicidal feelings. As one woman put it so poignantly, 'I feel like a mother with empty arms.' This is not to mention the callousness produced in others as a result.

Mr Christian, who felt strongly about this, nodded emphatically. 'Dr Francis Schaeffer sees a connection between abortion and child abuse. He observes that "if one can legally kill a child a few months before birth, one should not feel too bad about roughing him up a little bit (without killing him) after he is born."[2] Just as violence breeds violence so callousness breeds callousness.

'It's children who suffer so much,' he continued. 'My youngest daughter, Sharon, recently had to enter hospital for a minor operation. She was in a ward with three other thirteen year olds. Each of them was there because they had attempted suicide. One girl told Sharon why she'd done it. She said simply, "My parents always beat me up. Right from when I was a baby. I've had enough!"'

'I agree with you there that sexual self-gratification harms children,' said the Courier. 'One in three marriages ends in divorce and I know of one London borough where it's been reported that 25% of the children come from broken homes. That's a pretty disturbing statistic when you think what it

[1]Report of the working party of the Royal College of Obstetricians and Gynaecologists on Unplanned Pregnancies. Quoted in *Legal Abortion Examined.* (SPUC 1980)

[2] Francis Schaeffer, *Whatever happened to the human race?* (Marshall, Morgan & Scott, 1980)

leads to—the maladjustment, the confusion, the sorrow and rejection.'

'It puts me in mind of an old proverb I used to hear in Israel,' the Pilgrim Watcher said. ' "The fathers have eaten sour grapes, but the children's teeth are set on edge." ' He gazed penetratingly from beneath dark, lowering brows at both Mr Aquarius and Mr Christian. 'Any method you propose whereby people can be made whole must make that proverb unnecessary.'

With that he became invisible and the group parted for the night.

*   *   *

A Deptford car-breaker's yard might seem a strange place in which to conduct a conversation. The rusty, twisted wrecks of cars that had once been their owner's pride and joy now lay in derelict piles atop one another, wheelless and powerless; the burnt-out remains of a frenetic age, that for all its haste could not beat the speed of rust.

The four men picked their way across the spilled out mechanical intestines and organs which strewed the muddy track between the piles.

'I think this is an example of what Alvin Toffler calls "transient materialism",' the Courier puffed. 'Which is why I've brought you here. The important word behind what he's getting at is "new". It's no longer enough to own a car or a cooker, it's got to be a *new* one. It doesn't matter that the old one's still working all right, you've got to keep on changing it for a later model. You end up with the throwaway society, redundant technology, built-in obsolescence, "because nobody wants a car to last forever nowadays".'

'Let's sit over here,' Mr Christian suggested, indicating a couple of suitable car bonnets.

When they were comfortable, Mr Aquarius spoke to the Courier. 'Are you suggesting then that quality of life for today's materialist is measured not simply by the quantity of possessions he owns but also by their newness?'

'I am. And what's more I'd say that for most people a drop in the standard of living means not just that they can't buy more but that they can't replace all they'd like to either.'

'Your people are in desperate straits,' the Pilgrim Watcher observed. 'Is this why you always make haste to hurry backwards and forwards? You are all trying to keep up with this thing. Truly your belly god is a hungry monster!'

'That's the point I'm trying to make. It's basically idolatry,' Mr Christian insisted. 'Once the West rejected spiritual reality it was left only with this philosophy of self-gratification. People have to have some goals in life and most blindly serve this god.'

'Aren't you being a typical kill-joy Christian?' Mr Aquarius challenged. 'Surely it's not wrong to want a few comforts in life? After all, you can't deny that technical progress has benefited mankind no end.'

Mr Christian countered that it was not progress or comfort he was opposing but the way people have been duped into making a god of these things under such guises as "economic growth" and "raising the standard of living". Jesus, he reminded them, said that a man's life does not consist in the abundance of the things he possesses, but our society lives as though the opposite is the case.

This is the tragedy, to his mind. People are not happy, nor peaceful; on the contrary. For anxiety goes hand in hand with an abundance of possessions. Things need guarding, cleaning, servicing and renewing. Demanding gods! And many a family is split over money problems. Not only that, there are those who cannot handle the demands of greed and soon find themselves facing impossible debts and the accompanying despair, if not the very real temptation to crime.

He concluded, 'As a friend of mine put it, whilst walking down a well-heeled road in Blackheath, "I was envious of the rich, until I beheld their burglar alarms!" '

'So, it's really a great confidence trick with people believing that possessions bring happiness, even though they don't,' said Mr Aquarius. 'Well, that's fair enough. What I want to do, though, is to add a spiritual dimension to this materialism. I don't, of course, consider it idolatry in the negative way Mr Christian does. No, what I would do is to get a balance between the two aspects of reality so that people can enjoy the best of both worlds. Wholeness is to me a filling out of reality, not a denying of it.'

'I think you have not understood all that Mr Christian is saying,' the Pilgrim Watcher protested. 'But be that as it may for the moment. Mr Courier, I will ask you a question. How came this belief in materialism to win power over the minds of men, so that they serve it as a god?'

The Courier began with an illustration.

A market gardener, committed to growing as many peppers as possible, sooner or later produces a surplus of fruit. In order to dispose of them, somebody has to be persuaded to buy. The advertiser sets to work to convince people that not only will their quality of life be enhanced by eating peppers but actually depends upon it. The financier does his part and makes credit available, at interest, so that ordinary people can buy more peppers. In the words of Vance Packard, "The way to end glut was to produce gluttons". But where was this thing to end? What would happen when everyone had all they needed? Surely the market gardener would become bankrupt?

But this didn't happen because of the development of transient materialism. New technology kept producing new, improved versions of peppers. Designers kept the fashions changing. Red ones were in, then green ones; peppers with seeds, peppers without; big ones, small ones; long ones, squat ones. And if all else failed, built-in obsolescence ensured that the peppers rotted to pieces after so many days. People had to keep buying.

So, in spite of world recession, high unemployment,

inflation and commodity scarceness, all of which are brought about by materialism, the Western way of life has remained substantially intact.

'I have read that some of your Christian writers have prophesied that the economy of this country will be destroyed. They say it will happen soon.' The Pilgrim Watcher addressed Mr Christian. 'What think you of that?'

He replied, 'I believe that the present system contains the seeds of its own destruction and that, in the last days, that is just before Jesus returns, we shall see the fall of Babylon. I see this as materialistic society, whether capitalistic or communist. However, I'm not convinced that we are necessarily living in those days. The trouble with recession or any other crisis is that it always brings out the prophets of doom—including the Christian ones!'

He went on to explain that the belly god would not be overthrown merely by frightening people into thinking everything was about to collapse. There was a higher way, a better motivation to be found in Christian wholeness.

At that moment they were interrupted by a loud 'Oi'. They looked up to see a workman of grotesque proportions waddling towards them with a giggling blonde hanging on his arm.

'Wot you doin' 'ere?' he demanded. 'You've no right ter be nosin' around without my say so. Wot d'yer want anyway?'

'I'm awfully sorry,' began Mr Aquarius, 'but we just wanted a place to chat.'

The man swore and lit a cigarette. 'Well go and chat somewhere else. If yer don't want ter buy nuffink then get lost. Ah've got a livin' ter make an' ah don't want the likes of you 'anging abaht 'ere.'

Mumbling their apologies, the four made their exit. The man shouted after them: 'Oi, you ain't nicked nuffink 'av yer?'

His girl friend laughed.

'Do you think we've just met the belly god in person?' murmured the Courier.

*   *   *

The Courier and the Pilgrim Watcher stood on Tower Bridge looking upstream towards London Bridge. The Courier had a bachelor bedsit just south of the river in Tooley Street; the Pilgrim Watcher had requested his company this far because, as he said, bridges were good places for vanishing, and this was an exceptionally fine bridge. He also wished to have a private word with the Courier.

'You did not exaggerate when you described this society as thoroughly sick,' he said, 'You have demonstrated in full measure the lack of wholeness in the lives of the people. Such is always the bitter fruit of the Great Rebellion, but each age has its own particular way of bearing it.'

'Well, why have you bothered to come since you know what you're going to find?' the Courier queried. 'I confess I don't understand the ways of you Celestials, but I've learned not to argue any longer with the commands of God. You see, I do fear him.'

The Pilgrim Watcher nodded his approval.

'Then you have the beginning of wisdom,' he replied. 'Though you still search you will surely find the Lord Most High. Beyond that I may not influence you, for I am not of your kind. But I will answer your question. Much hinges on what happens in this age. Great forces are at work and we Celestials are being readied for the King's next great act. The Council have sent me to judge the progress of things, for we sense our own activities are to increase.'

The Courier confessed a slight apprehension at the thought of the Celestials being on the move. Would it be in judgement or in blessing, he wanted to know.

'That depends much upon the Children of the Firstborn, whom Mr Christian represents,' was the reply. 'If they awaken to full confidence at this time there shall be such blessing and healing as the world has never known. But if not, I fear the sickness will lead to death. More I cannot say.'

'What of Mr Aquarius? Who's he?'

'I confess I do not like him, for I know whom he serves, though he would not admit it, even to himself. He is dangerous because he is self-deceived—the worst kind of deception. Even now he influences some of the Children and they had best be wise to his guiles or they will be distracted from the Lamb's message. Many of them have yet to enter wholeness themselves and are easy prey to this different teaching. Mr Christian realizes this and you would do well to heed what he has to say, for I perceive you have need of the Lamb's touch yourself.'

The Courier nodded silently.

'I shall be gone a while,' the Pilgrim Watcher added. 'I hope on my return that you will have listened well and found your desire.'

With that he leapt the iron balustrade before the Courier's startled eyes, but there was no splash in the waters below. He had gone. The Courier blinked and turned for home just as the five o'clock commuter stampede was beginning. Tomorrow, he and Mr Christian would hear what Mr Aquarius had to say. Meanwhile, he had a lot of thinking to do.

CHAPTER THREE

The Aquarian Alternative

The Courier and Mr Christian were sitting on cushions in a beautifully decorated room which was part of a rambling old house in Penge. Mr Aquarius' wife, Dawn, sat cross-legged opposite them. On the sofa were a dark, gypsyish girl named Karen and a demure young woman called Susan. A lanky chap named Tony was sprawled in a corner. The walls of the room were tastefully adorned with peace symbols and mystic paintings. A joss-stick smouldered on the table. This was Mr Aquarius' commune and the group had gathered, at his invitation, to debate their ideas on health and wholeness. Though slightly put out by the non-appearance of the Pilgrim Watcher, Mr Aquarius set about introducing everybody, and soon they were all on first name terms (Dai Thomas the Courier, Peter Christian and Leo Aquarius). Then he opened up the debate.

'We've seen enough to realize that society is sick and in desperate need of healing. Yet this immediately raises the question of how such a situation can have come about when we have a National Health Service in which millions of pounds and thousands of jobs are invested, and which has access to the finest scientific and technical discoveries the world has yet to offer.

'Now, if we ask Mr Average what he thinks is wrong, the

chances are he'll criticize the quality of the service the N.H.S. provides. He'll talk of people having to wait ridiculously long times for operations and even consultations, of feeling themselves pushed from one department to another by an impersonal bureaucracy which treats them like cars to be serviced rather than people to be healed. He may well view the medical profession itself as an elite, self-protecting group unwilling to treat patients as people with a right to know what's going on. There's an increasing feeling of, "What's the use of going to the doctor? He'll only give me some tablets or send me for an X-ray." People are losing faith in the system.

'This in itself says something. It indicates that the man-in-the-street has come to expect the N.H.S. to be responsible for his health and well-being. That's why he gets so upset when it doesn't live up to his expectations. In other words, the N.H.S. has educated him to be passive.

'I'm not denying, for a moment, the good that has been done—only a fool would do that—but I am nonetheless questioning this whole approach.'

In days of government cutbacks and widespread unrest within the N.H.S. (all of which should be deplored, if only because bad atmosphere hinders healing) it is all too easy to forget the thousands of ordinary lives saved each year and the overwhelmingly successful treatment of many ailments. Since its introduction in 1948 the N.H.S. must take significant credit for the drop in infant mortality, the rise in life expectancy and the virtual abolition of the great scourges of the past. Let the man in the street fall prey to a road accident and he will swiftly appreciate the benefits of free conventional medicine!

'May I just say that I agree with you wholeheartedly, on your point about passivity,' Mr Christian interjected. 'I've long maintained that to call it a health service is a misnomer. Really it should be called the National Sickness Service because instead of teaching people how to live in health, thereby preventing disease, it spends the majority of its resources trying to remedy things when they go wrong.'

'You mean if only the Health Service had taught people how to live without stress, how to eat properly, how to improve the environment and the like, then there would be much less illness?' asked the Courier.

'Yes, that's the sort of thing I mean. Though, to be honest, I believe it's the Christian gospel which is the real key to health,' he replied.

'Hey, man, if that's so, how come you Christians have got thousands of people in the health services? Why ain't you all pulled out?' drawled Tony from the corner.

Mr Christian explained that believers had always led the way in caring for needy people so it was natural for them to be involved in the medical profession. In any case, it was the Christian view of the world which had made possible scientific and medical advances in the first place. Unless we believe in an ordered universe and a God who provides good things for mankind, there is neither the possibility of research nor any point in it. Western science has been built on this premise.

One of the problems which Christians in the medical profession face today, he pointed out, is that modern man has moved away from that biblical base. He no longer honours God nor depends upon him for wisdom. This has led to a loss of moral absolutes and to terrible dilemmas, especially in medical research. So, in one laboratory scientists might be sluicing live embryos down the drain as they experiment on the genetic code in an attempt to obviate congenital deformity. Next door doctors may be caring for the life of a premature baby while in yet another room an unneccessary abortion is being performed. This kind of confusion raises the question as to whether the time is not ripe for Christians to pull out and produce a Christ-centred alternative on morally clear ground.

'If you did that, would you then concentrate on preventive medicine?' asked Susan.

Mr Christian nodded. 'We want to put a lot of emphasis

on prevention by means of a healthy lifestyle that's based
on the work of Christ. We also believe in the power of divine
healing. But that still leaves a place for medical treatment,
though used in a way that's dependent on the Lord. I guess
we want to stress the divine art of healing rather than
simply trust in the science of medicine.'

'I'm glad you said that,' Mr Aquarius came in, 'because
what we believe is wrong with orthodox medicine is the way
it treats man just as a machine and relies upon merely
physical scientific treatments to the neglect of a true healing
which involves the spiritual dimensions as well.'

Mr Aquarius went on to say that he felt things had
developed in this way partly because of an over-commit-
ment to the 'germ theory' of disease. This views sickness as
an attack by alien organisms which need defeating by a
chemical or surgical counterattack, because the body is
generally considered to be too weak or too ineffective to
defend itself. So, in spite of all the attendant risks, conventional medicine consists of developing ever more powerful
drugs and sophisticated surgical techniques to fight this war.

'There are, of course, diseases which are congenital in
origin, as well as those acquired through injury,' interjected
the Courier.

'The medical profession deludes itself into thinking that
everything can be cured in this violent way,' said Dawn.
'Even mental problems and crime are brought under the
same kind of treatment.'

'White coated, sterile witch doctors; the high priests of a
stainless steel society,' murmured the Courier.

'Yes, and like all religious elites they are very protective
of their trade. That's why they don't like our way,' said
Karen. 'After all, it would put them out of a job!'

Mr Aquarius declared that he felt the time had come to
share the thinking behind his alternative approach.

He proceeded to describe what he called a *holistic* outlook
on life and the treatment of sickness. He explained that
'holistic' comes from the Greek word '*holos*' meaning whole.

Instead of viewing man as a machine, the holistic practitioner takes account of mind, body and spirit. These three aspects of personality are inter-related and together make up a living energy system which is in a continuous state of flux with the life-force of the cosmos. Because there are no rigid boundaries between the parts this constant flow of life-energy causes one part to affect another. For example, an interference in the spiritual dimension may cause illness in the physical and vice versa.

A good state of health exists when there are no blocks or contradictions in the energy flow. Hence, holistic medicine concentrates both on teaching how to maintain a proper energy balance and how to restore it if it is lost. Preventive techniques, he explained, include suitable diet, relaxation methods and mood monitoring. Healing therapies may be of a semi-physical kind, such as acupuncture or massage, or be wholly psychic, as with absent healing.

'Our methods avoid two of the main pitfalls of orthodox medicine,' Dawn chipped in. 'We teach people to take active steps with regard to their well-being and when they do need healing we involve ourselves with their whole being. People feel both responsible and also cared for.'

'I can vouch for that,' declared Susan. 'I went to the doctor with severe back pain. He gave me some painkillers and told me to rest. Well, the pain didn't go away so when I returned he sent me to the hospital for some X-rays. I had to wait two weeks for those and another six weeks to see a consultant. Nobody seemed to care that I was in agony all that time. When I did see him, eventually, the X-rays were lost and I had to have more done. The consultant wasn't sure whether it was a slipped disc or sciatica or what, so he gave me more painkillers and suggested some physiotherapy. I felt he didn't believe me anyway.'

'And what happened?' asked the Courier.

'The physiotherapy department said I would have to wait a month. So I walked out in disgust. Then I met Karen. She offered to treat my back and, bingo, the pain was gone! So I came here and they're teaching me how to relax now and to strengthen my spine so it doesn't happen again. It works!'

Dawn explained that Susan had been a Christian believer but all her minister had done was to tell her to go to the doctor and promise to mention it at the prayer meeting. He had been very cross with Susan when she later told him how she had been healed.

'That's what gets me with you Christians, man,' Tony called from the corner. 'You send people to the doctors' because you've got no answers yourselves. Then you complain when somebody else does the job properly in a way you don't like!'

Mr Christian felt extremely concerned that Susan should be in this group but acknowledged Tony's point as graciously as he could, saying that not all Christians were so powerless and many were developing alternative medicine themselves.

'You mean they're in the same thing we're into?' he replied.

'Some are dabbling in your kind of treatments because they too are dissatisfied with orthodox medicine. But I'm not happy with that, for all sorts of reasons. Others of us are discovering an alternative which at some points has similarities with yours but is actually quite different—and I feel it's very important for Christians to understand those differences.'

'Why aren't you happy with what these people are doing?' Susan asked cautiously. 'Do you think it's all occult?'

'Yes, but not in the way that you imagine,' he answered. 'People…'

Before he could continue there was a loud outburst from the other members of the commune.

'There you go again,' Tony expostulated. 'That's your answer to everything that's new or different. Blame it on the devil!'

'You'll be burning us at the stake next for using herbal

remedies!' cried Dawn. The others nodded.

Mr Aquarius spoke more calmly, 'I feel you make a mistake when you accuse us of occultism, Peter. I don't deny that many of our practices originated in superstitious and religious societies but we've purified them of those things. Don't forget, either, that orthodox medicine also has so-called occult roots. But you don't refuse to give digitalis to a patient with high blood pressure just because it was used by superstitious gypsies in bygone days in the form of foxgloves. Really, you must stop writing us off like this.'

'What is this life-force then if it's not some kind of religious being?' asked the Courier.

Mr Aquarius said he didn't personally believe in a universe full of spirits and gods but he did believe in a cosmic Ultimate Life Force. Some people, he felt, called this God, others described it as Spirit. More primitive peoples turned it into a world of good and bad angels. But, in fact, the Force is neutral; it's no more than the non-material, psychic or spiritual aspect of reality.

The problem with modern man, he went on to say, is that he has not only rejected traditional religion but anything he cannot see with his own eyes. So he only experiences a part of reality and this has grave consequences when it comes to the matter of health. Thankfully, scientists are beginning to recognize the true nature of the universe and a lot of experiments are being performed in the areas of extra-sensory perception, telepathy, telekinesis and so forth, which are proving the existence of a non-physical aspect to reality.

'If only we could all realize this,' Karen added earnestly, 'we'd solve the problems of mankind. Once we learn to tap into the life-force we'll come into harmony with our whole environment.'

'The trouble with materialists is that they treat the world as an enemy to be conquered, so they're violent people. That's why the Piscean age was to be characterized by Jesus' message of love—it needed it,' said Dawn. 'But we're at the beginning of a new age, the Aquarian age of harmony, when we shall not need to love our enemies because, by becoming one with ourselves and our *total* environment, we shall no longer be enemies. The lion shall lie down with the lamb,' she concluded triumphantly.

By now, Mr Christian was fairly bursting to speak and wanted to challenge all these ideas. But he reluctantly submitted to the Courier's suggestion that he wait until after the tea break to have his say. When the Courier discovered it was herb tea they were going to drink, he wondered at his own advice!

*   *   *

After the break Mr Christian began.

'We obviously have a fair bit of agreement over the current state of conventional medicine and its effect on patients. But we strongly disagree over the alternative. You didn't like my suggesting to Susan here that your approach is demonic, but you never gave me a chance to explain what I meant by that; so I'll try to now, if I may.

'Most people, when they think of demons and the occult, have in mind what they've picked up from films like *The Exorcist* or from lurid stories about naked covens prancing in the woods. Now that's one aspect of it but not at all what I mean when I say there are demons at work behind your kind of medicine.'

In order to explain what he did mean, he read Colossians chapter 2 verse 8: 'See to it that no one makes a prey of you by philosophy and empty deceit, according to human tradition, according to the elemental spirits of the universe, and not according to Christ.'

'Paul is teaching that humanistic thoughts and ideas are not as neutral as we like to imagine. There are spiritual forces at work behind the basic philosophic assumptions upon which man builds his society. There are two which I think are particularly important.

'The first is the elemental spirit behind the teaching of the ancient Greek philosopher, Plato. Plato said that reality was spiritual—in other words, the non-material world is the most important part. I should point out that he did not mean spiritual in the way Christians use the term. The influence of that spirit is especially seen in the Eastern, mystical religions.

'The other doctrine is that taught by Aristotle, another Greek, who said the opposite to Plato. He claimed that reality was only the visible, material world and his influence is apparent in Western culture. Again, I believe there's a spirit which motivates this philosophy, and one which has particularly sought to deny the reality of the true spiritual world in order to undermine the Christian faith.

'Now Western man, having ceased to believe in Christianity and living in what some have called "the post-Christian age" has also found his materialism unsatisfying. So he has turned East in the hope of finding meaning to life in mysticism. Now if I understand you correctly, you're seeking to fuse the two ideas of reality into one scientific mysticism.'

Mr Aquarius acknowledged that this was so.

'Then I believe what you're doing is compounding your error. Instead of following one elemental spirit you're believing in two! And this is all the more subtle because it gives you some appearance of spirituality, yet without any reference to God or Christ. It's a most dangerous counterfeit.'

Here he looked pointedly at Susan who shifted uncomfortably on her seat. The atmosphere was by now distinctly hostile.

The Courier wanted to know why Christians saw this development in terms of spirits while the others thought of it as 'forces'.

To answer the point Mr Christian directed their attention to C.S. Lewis' prophetic foresight when in 1942 he wrote in *The Screwtape Letters* about the coming of 'the Materialist-

Magician'. C.S.Lewis described this as a satanic master-stroke. The devil, he said, would have people worshipping Forces whilst denying the existence of spirits. This would play right into his hands, for he is at his most dangerous when people do not believe he exists.

Mr Christian continued, 'Ever since Eve believed the lie, "You shall be as gods," man has been open to the temptation to believe that spiritual power resides in himself. He believes he has innate abilities which can be developed by the right practices. I say that all he is doing is opening himself up to being used by spirits, without realizing it.

'The purpose is plain. Materialism kept people from God by denying all spiritual reality. Now that has failed, Satan tries to convince us that our spiritual power is autonomous. If we think that, we can interpret all the great religious figures of history—Moses, Elijah, Christ, Buddha—in a new light. We can look upon them as great mystical figures and believe that we can be like them if only we will learn to develop *our* psychic powers. It panders to human pride and keeps us from true spirituality. Actually, it's another religion, one which has no place for repentance or the cross of Christ or fellowship with the living God.'

Needless to say, these words did not go down at all well in that company and in the tense silence which followed Mr Christian's remarks, Mr Aquarius announced lunch. Susan was visibly disturbed by what she had heard and asked Mr Christian if she could talk with him after lunch. He gladly agreed, and so, after a subdued vegetarian meal they went for a walk together, to the annoyance, it may be said, of Dawn.

'You've shaken me quite a bit by what you've been saying, Peter,' she began. 'I find it difficult because they really are nice people and they seem to care for me more than my church. Now you're telling me they're evil, demon-possessed people.'

'I didn't say they are any more evil than other unbelievers,' he replied gently. 'But they're deceived in a particularly dangerous way, and it's a way which is beginning to affect large numbers of people who are looking for answers to materialism. I'm not denying, either, that they have good intentions towards you, Susan. Though I feel Dawn would coax you right away from the church because she believes it harms you.'

'Hmm, I can see what you're saying about them and it does make sense from a Christian standpoint. But why do you think it's harmful for me to be getting into this scene?'

He explained that there were two reasons why it was dangerous for Christians. The first was that it was 'tuning in' to the lower spiritual realm, crossing a gulf which should not be crossed. She should beware of anything that was not 'according to Christ' and ought to repent of this involvement with the Enemy however unwitting it may have been.

The second reason was to do with legalism and legalistic spirits.

'I didn't go into this earlier,' he chuckled, 'because I knew I'd already set the cat among the pigeons, but there's a terrific amount of legalism in the "New Age Movement", and the Bible tells us that these "elemental spirits" are behind that as well. Do you know what the apostle Paul said?' He quoted from memory, ' "If with Christ you died to the elemental spirits of the universe, why do you live as if you still belonged to the world? Why do you submit to regulations...according to human precepts and doctrines?" (Colossians 2:20–22). You know, the Lord delivered you from rule-keeping when he saved you, Susan. He doesn't want you to become a slave again!'

'I think I understand that, but can you give me some examples of where you feel these people are submitting to legalistic spirits?' she answered.

They found a wall to sit on in a sunny spot and he took the issue of biorhythms as an example.

Biorhythms is the name given to describe human performance cycles. Most people are aware of ups and downs in their lives. There are times when they feel especially alert mentally, for example, and other times when they can hardly cope with the newspaper headlines. The same goes for emotional and physical states.

The theory behind biorhythms is that these changes in physical, mental and emotional states follow definite cycles which begin at birth and continue throughout life. Research has shown that the intellectual cycle lasts thirty-three days, the emotional twenty-eight days and the physical twenty-three days. Each cycle has an active phase when energies are high and a passive one when they are low. The change-over times are periods of unstable energy supply. So, a typical biorhythmic chart will look something like this.

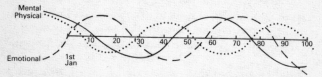

Sometimes these charts are plotted in conjunction with a person's star-signs and tied in with astrological forecasts, but not always.

Mr Christian said he had no real problem with the idea of cycles of ups and downs. After all, most Christian women of child-bearing age are used to their monthly cycles, which are a God-given way of renewing the body and preparing it for the possibility of conception—and there are mood changes which accompany this process! However, he was not happy with the concept of biorhythms.

Susan acknowledged that she had been given a bio-rhythmic chart together with her star forecast. She confessed that she'd been a little unhappy about the latter.

'I strongly advise you to forget about the whole thing,' he replied. 'It'll only bring you into bondage, for that's the satanic intention behind it.'

'But aren't biorhythms scientifically true?' she protested.

'There's been a fair amount of research carried out but as with all these surveys it is difficult to be dogmatic,' he replied. 'The most significant piece of research I know of was that carried out by the U.S. Navy, but then the men involved were already used to a regimented life, so I don't know if they were not predisposed to regular cycles. Anyway, that's not the real point. Why have you got a chart in the first place, even supposing it's accurate?'

'Well, so that I can plan my life according to my anticipated state,' she replied.

'But that's not how the Lord tells us to organize our lives,' he answered. 'He taught us to pray and to plan in dependence upon him so that we do his will, not what we suppose will be most comfortable or successful for us.'

Susan looked down at her feet.

'Do you remember what Paul said? "When I am weak, then I am strong" (2 Corinthians 12:10). It may well be that God will want you to do the very thing your biorhythms say you shouldn't do, so that the power and grace of God might be demonstrated in you. After all, the Lord told Paul, "My grace is sufficient for you, for my power is made perfect in weakness" ' (2 Corinthians 12:9).

Susan nodded.

'I see that, I suppose, but where do the spirits come into it?'

He explained the connection between spirits and seasons. Galatians chapter 4:8–10 says, 'Formerly when you did not know God, you were in bondage to beings that by nature are no gods; but now that you have come to know God, or rather to be known by God, how can you turn back again to the weak and beggarly elemental spirits, whose slaves you want to be once more? You observe days, and months, and seasons and years!'

Behind this slavish organizing of life around special Jewish days and ceremonies there lay spirits of legalism, bringing people into a bondage over what they could or could not do. It gave them a framework for life but took away both the freedom and the dependence upon the Lord which the new covenant brings. That vital fellowship in the

Spirit is so precious that nothing should be allowed to come in its place. Biorhythms is another, secular, legalism, which is motivated by the same pathetic spirits which sought to bring the Galatian Christians away from their simple relationship with the Lord.

Susan smiled as she took a folded piece of paper from her pocket. She looked at it wryly.

'Today I'm supposed to be physically up, emotionally so-so and mentally unstable! I think I'll try to trust the Lord to look after me instead. Take this will you, Peter, because I think I'll find it hard to dispose of otherwise.'

He tore the paper into small pieces for her.

As they wandered back towards the house he asked Susan if she had become a vegetarian.

'More or less,' she replied. 'I still get a craving for meat sometimes, so I eat fish. But I'm not one of those vegans who won't touch any animal produce, not even eggs and milk. I think that's going too far.'

'Are all the household vegetarians?'

'Yes, but for different reasons. Tony, for example, says the thought of blood makes him feel sick. Dawn is a campaigner against cruelty to animals. I think Karen and Leo feel it heightens their psychic awareness.'

'And you...?'

'I don't know really. It's healthier I suppose. Apparently there are all sorts of toxins which meat eating produces in our bodies which can induce cancer and heart diseases—as well as the high fat content causing obesity. Don't you agree with that?' she asked.

'The whole subject is a big one and I'd like to invite you to hear me out on that some other day. Actually, I do feel we'd be better eating less meat than we do in the West. But again what I'm concerned about are the legalistic spirits which ban meat-eating, or any other food for that matter, on the grounds that it makes you a morally or spiritually better person.'

'You mean like Leo and Karen?'

'Yes, you see the real answer to the lower passions—and vegetarians claim their diet reduces aggression—is the Holy Spirit. "Walk by the Spirit and do not gratify the desires of the flesh" (Galatians 5:16). That scripture I quoted from Colossians 2 back in the house goes on to say, "These have indeed an appearance of wisdom in promoting rigour of devotion and self-abasement and severity to the body, but they are of no value in checking the indulgence of the flesh" (Colossians 2:23). It's another one of these deceptions to draw us away from Christ.'

By this time they had reached the commune and they let the subject drop as they entered. The Courier wondered where they had been and, Mr Christian fancied, was especially concerned for Susan. At least, he made sure he sat next to her that afternoon. Mr Aquarius began to speak.

'This morning Peter delivered what I suppose he must consider a body blow to our whole philosophy. If you accept that, then almost anything else I say will have to be rejected.

'The only response I can give really is to say that if I'm Aquarian then he's antiquarian! Really these notions about demons are quite outmoded—primitive religious ways of explaining the difficulties of life. I'm surprised you want to blame spirits for *ideas*, Peter. That really is committing intellectual suicide! No, insights come to men as they study and meditate—and real wisdom comes to those who open themselves to the whole cosmic reality. *That's* revelation; not this stuff about God speaking through a book, let alone evil spirits leading us astray.

'If there's any value in religion it's the enlightenment some have gained which can help us to live better today. But that doesn't mean that gods actually exist. What religious people give names to are just the psychic aspects of life. Strip away this superstition and you're left with the pure insight. I'll give you an example.

'When we first met (he addressed the Courier and Mr Christian) we spent a fair deal of time on the subject of stress and agreed that all the current remedies were passive. In fact, they're typically Western, materialistic answers. Now I'm going to suggest that we look East to a culture which has, for centuries, used a different and positive remedy. I mean meditation.'

Mr Christian was not surprised to find Mr Aquarius was well into transcendental meditation. This is a yoga-derived form of self-induced trance-like state whose origins are deep in Hinduism. It was popularized in the West by the Maharishi Mahesh Yogi, a follower of Guru Dat. In 1967 the Maharishi took the Beatles to India and taught them this Vedic practice.

T.M. claims to lift people into a state of 'bliss consciousness' or 'pure awareness' where they are tuned in to 'creative intelligence'. Evidence of lowered heart rate and blood pressure and an increase of alpha waves in the brain made this a sure-fire hit with those wanting to reduce the pressures of the Western lifestyle. Religious terminology was cloaked in the language of science and psychology and the movement flourished. Centres sprang up everywhere and institutions began to take the claims seriously, especially in the U.S.A. That is, until 1979 when the American Congress ruled that T.M. was a religion and that, therefore, under the Second Amendment of the Constitution it could neither be taught in schools or be government-funded.

A devotee chants his mantra, a secret word given to him after a Hindu initiation ceremony, twenty minutes in the morning and twenty minutes at night. All thought is to be subjugated to the sound and rhythm of the chant so that a state of tranquillity comes about. After 73,500 minutes of meditation the disciple can hope for full union with Being. When challenged that this was pure Hinduism, Mr Aquarius neither affirmed nor denied it. What mattered, he said, was that it effectively reduced tension and made for more creative living. That was the insight; the religious origin was unimportant.

'To my mind it's an extremely dangerous technique,' Mr

Christian said. 'You're not going to like this, but I believe this mind emptying process opens you up to possession by demons, particularly the seducing kind which foster a pseudo-spirituality, with no real knowledge of the living God. In the end you'll be eaten up by spiritual snobbery.'

'Here we go again!' groaned Tony from his corner.

'But surely Christians believe in meditation?' Susan questioned. 'So what's the difference? I mean, I can see your objection to worshipping Hindu gods but if meditation is purified from this and used purely as a relaxing, expanding exercise, surely that's all right?'

'The difference between this kind of meditation and Christian meditation is to do with content.' Mr Christian replied. 'Leo empties his mind and has an experience similar to an L.S.D. trip but he can't explain it; it's mystical and the nearest he can get to a description is to talk of oneness with the Cosmos. Christians, when they meditate, do so upon the "true truths" of Scripture and they have fellowship with a God who is actually there and who can be described in moral and personal terms.' He smiled. 'My meditation is both with and upon a Person. In fact, it's a two-way communication. I may add that all the psychological and physical benefits are there, as well as true spiritual experience. But they're welcome spin-offs rather than the motive for meditation. I dwell on the Lord because I love him and he loves me.'

'You're going to treat my yoga in the same way, aren't you?' said Dawn. 'Because I use it for the same purpose as Leo but with the additional benefit of getting physically fit.'

He nodded.

The Courier had a question for Mr Christian.

'I can see what you're getting at when yoga is practised in this way, Peter, but don't many people attend yoga classes *purely* for the physical benefits without all the mystical undertones? Do you feel that's wrong for Christians?'

'I do actually, because the very nature of yoga doesn't allow the occult–mystical element to be removed, only reduced. And in the long run, if a person is going to get anywhere with it, he will be drawn into the dangerous element. It's the folly of Western materialism to imagine that we can despiritualize everything to extract only what we want. That assumes there are no spiritual beings behind the scenes who have their own sinister intentions. According to the Bible there's a direct connection between idolatry or false religion, and demons. Paul talks about it in 1 Corinthians 10:19–20.

'There are many forms of yoga all based on Hindu belief. The word comes from the Sanskrit *yuj* meaning "to unite". This reveals the true purpose of yoga which is to unite a personality within itself and with god. It is an alternative religion which denies sin as the cause of fragmentation and stress. Essentially, it turns a person in on himself to find salvation and denies the need for Christ's death.'

Hat-ha yoga, the form most commonly taught in the West, is one of eight pantheistic yoga disciplines which lead to union. Its teachers believe that each time we breathe there is a conflict between two warring impulses, hence our restlessness. If we can unite these we will be free to concentrate on our True Self. This united life energy *(prana)* needs pushing down to the base of the spine where it can enter one of the seven spiritual energy centres *(chakras)*. Once this is achieved, spiritual life becomes easier and many spiritual options become open to us. Strictly, the health benefits are by-products.

'The postures and the encouragements to relax and empty the mind are the means designed to achieve this religious goal,' he continued. 'Bearing in mind that there are spirits behind all this it seems utter folly for a Christian to expose himself in such a way, and I know some people who have needed to be freed from satanic oppression because of their involvement with yoga.'

Dawn sneered but he continued, addressing the Courier and Susan in particular.

'There are far more effective ways of getting fit which

have none of these risks. When a person tells me they are thinking of taking up yoga purely for health reasons I always ask, "Why yoga?" People are not always honest with themselves. What they're really seeking is something more; there is a spiritual hunger which wants satisfying— and I have a better answer to that!'

Mr Aquarius rounded off the proceedings none too happily. 'I had hoped that we might have found some common ground so that we could present a united answer to this world's problems. Indeed, I had thought Christians were more tolerant, more enlightened and open-minded to other ways these days, but it seems I was wrong. You're dogmatic in insisting that we're a demon-inspired human-istic religious movement with which you can have no dealings. Fair enough, but I just hope you've got something better to offer. What I've seen of Christianity doesn't impress me very much. You all seem as uptight, unbalanced and unfit as everyone else!'

'Yeah,' said Tony.

'Well, I think you should hear Peter out,' said the Courier. 'You can have plenty of opportunity to question him.'

'I can't see any point in that at all,' snapped Dawn. 'I've heard quite enough. He's got his mind made up.'

'But so have you,' the Courier protested. 'You're just as intolerant, you know.'

'I would like to hear what Peter has to say,' said Susan quietly. 'Even if I disagree with him.'

Dawn was incensed.

'You'll be making a big mistake. Before you know it you'll be right back where you started. And your back will probably get bad again. What will they do for you? Pray in their prayer meeting!'

The Courier was cross. 'That's very unkind, if you don't mind my saying so.' He turned to Susan. 'I'll be going along to hear Peter preach on Sunday. Would you like to come with me?'

'I'd like that very much,' she smiled into his eyes.

Mr Christian breathed a sigh of relief as he left the house with the Courier and he prayed Susan would come along to church. A faint haze of light caught their attention at that moment; the Pilgrim Watcher had not been as absent as they had imagined. They grinned, then laughed.

'See you soon then, Dai.'

'Okay, boyo,' he replied cheerfully.

*   *   *

The next Sunday the Courier and Susan attended Mr Christian's church to hear him preach on a positive Christian answer to both Western materialism and New Age Consciousness. Mr Aquarius did not come.

CHAPTER FOUR

Biblical Wholeness

The congregation took their seats as the glorious crescendo of praise died away. The worship had blown the Courier's mind and stirred the very depths of his being. Never had he experienced such a sense of the nearness of God; it was as though heaven and earth had met and he was in the very presence of the praising hosts. For the first time in his life he was experiencing, though from the edge, something of the unutterable joy which fills the hearts of Christians. And what singing! The simple melodies soon had his Welsh tenor voice soaring in praise of the majesty of Christ, singing softly of the melting love of the Father, thrilling to the march-songs of the saints.

Susan was not so blessed for she was of those who had been taught by silent, solemn example not to display emotion in worship. The freedom of form had left her floundering at times, though she was honest enough to recognize that nothing was out of control. Indeed, she had been impressed by the genuine depth and order which underlay the proceedings. But it was *so* different.

The Pilgrim Watcher was there but certainly not on the ground. He had danced and cried the praises of the Most High in the lofty expanse above the congregation, along with the company of praising angels appointed to serve and protect those saints. He was in his element!

As everyone settled down, Mr Christian stood to address them.

'For quite a number of years my wife and I rented a rustic chalet in the ancient hamlet of Swyre, in Dorset, for our family holiday. The place has fond memories and none more so for me than sitting by the window in the evening surrounded by the smell of pinewood, watching the setting sun cast long shadows over the hazy green hills, listening to the gentle sound of grazing sheep. Add three lovely children tucked up in bed after a glorious day on the beach, a beautiful wife by my side, a glass of cider in my hand and a John Williams' guitar concerto in the background, and there you have it—absolute bliss! It's not difficult at such times to agree with David's immortal words in Psalm 23. "He leads me beside still waters."

'But life isn't like that most of the time, is it? We live in a frenetic world made ugly by sin, overstressed to breaking point, indulging itself to death, and godless in the extreme. Surely David's experience is relevant only to rare moments in our existence? Is that perhaps why this psalm is quoted more at funerals than anywhere else? Nobody expects to *live* like that any more! The age of such tranquillity has passed into the realms of nostalgia. In the real world we have to survive as best we can.

'Or is that really so? David's life wasn't, in fact, very easy. Minding sheep could be a perilous business at the best of times, let alone when you were treated as the dogsbody by the rest of your family. To become a popular hero overnight only to find yourself a political refugee outlawed by a mentally unstable king couldn't have been easy either; nor could the heartbreak of your one close friend and ally dying in battle. That is to say nothing of ruling a tiny kingdom whose strategic geography made it the target for every ambitious nation round about. Nonetheless, in the midst of all this David had discovered an inner peace and equilibrium which not only freed him from fear and foreboding but filled him with a joy so overwhelming that it could not be quenched by even the worst times. He had discovered God's wholeness.

'What David experienced is the will of God for every one of us. It's not a special experience for the favoured few but for all who love our Lord Jesus Christ. But how many of us live like this? So often we're content with an assurance of heaven but have little expectation of living significantly different lives from those of the unbelievers about us. Far too many Christians suffer stress and anxiety. Few have positive expectation of good health as a spiritual birthright. Saints sometimes seem as doctor-dependent as sinners. Many others are caught up with self-indulgent habits, and our lifestyles in general tend to conform with those of our neighbours instead of expressing the radical nature of the kingdom of God. For these reasons, I want to make two points. The first concerns what wholeness is and the second is about how it's achieved.

'God has given us a tremendous promise in Ezekiel 37:26. He says, "I will make a covenant of peace with them; it shall be an everlasting covenant with them." This promise expressed the great hope which runs through the Old Testament like a silver thread. Even at the time of Jerusalem's downfall, Jeremiah could still assert it, "Behold, I will bring to it health and healing, and I will heal them; and I will reveal to them an abundance of peace and truth" (Jeremiah 33:6 NASB).

'Now I want us to understand that the word translated here as "peace" is the Hebrew word *shalom*. Shalom means much more than calmness. It includes the whole sense of inner unity, poise and completeness. This inner shalom is the source of all outward wholeness. If your soul is in shalom then you may expect everything else to be blessed. John expressed it in his desire for Gaius, "I pray that in all respects you may prosper and be in good health, *just as* your soul prospers" (3 John 2). Whenever we read of peace in our Bibles we may almost always understand it to have this sense of personal wholeness.

'Wholeness isn't really an optional extra,' he continued.
'In fact, it's another way of expressing true holiness. What a
pity that we've come to view holiness as unhealthy and
miserable! True holiness makes us like Jesus. It has relatively
little to do with how many hours we spend praying and
reading the Bible or how many sins we *don't* commit. It has
an awful lot to do with being an internally united person,
walking in joyous harmony with God and his people. It
means a sound mind, wholesome emotions and a spirit at
rest. It includes proper care and use of a body which is
nothing less than the temple of the Holy Spirit. And it
means changing our personal and corporate environment
until it reflects the kingdom of God, for, "Of the increase of
his government and of *shalom* there shall be no end" (Isaiah
48:22). Let's broaden our horizons to grasp the full extent of
God's glorious salvation and seek to enter into that.'

He proceeded to show that wholeness is only possible in
relation to righteousness and directed their attention to
Psalm 85:8,10, 'He will speak peace to his people...Steadfast
love and faithfulness will meet; *righteousness and peace* will
kiss each other.' On the other hand, 'There is no peace
(shalom, wholeness) for the wicked.' The fundamental
mistake people like Mr Aquarius make is to assume that
wholeness can be obtained without reference to
righteousness. According to the Bible, the root cause of all
our brokenness is our separation from God because of sin.
'None is righteous...no one seeks for God...they have gone
wrong...in their paths are ruin and misery, *and the way of
peace* they do not know' (Romans 3:11–17). 'They live blind-
fold in a world of illusion, and are cut off from the life of
God...(Ephesians 4:18, PHILLIPS).

'That first rebellion by Adam and Eve was catastrophic.
It cut them off from God himself; it brought suspicion, fear
and embarrassment into their relationship with each other.
They were broken up on the inside and became full of
conflicting desires as sin brought disintegration to their

personalities. They became slaves of Satan, obligated to do his will in spite of a conscience which cried otherwise.

'Even creation itself was marred. Futility entered the cosmos with earthquake, famine and flood. Nature became "red in tooth and claw"; death stalked the globe. Life became a fight for survival and the years brought grimness to man as he strove to eke an existence from the dust to which he was doomed to return.

'Their offspring have fared no better. Paul writes in Ephesians 2:1–3, "You were dead through the trespasses and sins in which you once walked, following the course of this world, following the prince of the power of the air, the spirit that is now at work in the sons of disobedience. Among these we all once lived in the passions of our flesh, following the desires of body and mind, and so we were by nature children of wrath, like the rest of mankind." I say again that true wholeness only comes as this problem of unrighteousness is solved. No humanistic solution is ever going to work. Which brings me to my second point.

'God's answer is not a new philosophy or doctrine, nor a fresh set of rules for living. His remedy is a new Man who will be the first-born of a whole race of people who have received his nature in exchange for their broken lives. His name is Jesus of Nazareth and he is the one truly whole man who ever lived.'

Mr Christian explained how the world had waited long years for the coming of this Anointed One, enduring many frauds, trying many alternatives. Misunderstandings about him were so great that the Son of God slipped unnoticed into the very society chosen to receive him and neither the religious, political nor intellectual leaders of the day were prepared to accept him.

'Not that this was a mistake on God's part,' he continued. 'Jesus was to be received by faith, not by sight. People could easily imagine a monk from the mystic mountains of Tibet to be the Messiah or even the slick business-orientated pretenders who offer their humble followers world domination in exchange for a temporary period of suffering for the cause. But Jesus was like none of these.

'The miracle of the incarnation lies not simply in the virgin conception but in the *ordinariness* of Jesus. Born in neither a palace nor an ascetic community, his parents not wealthy or excessively poor, receiving the normal education of his day along with brothers and sisters, he learned the family trade like generations of others. How do we know he is the Son of God, except by revelation?

'One who received such revelation was the apostle John, a man closer to Jesus than any other. He wrote, "The Word became flesh and dwelt among us, full of grace and truth; we have beheld his glory, glory as of the only Son from the Father" (John 1:14). The glory of Jesus lay in his being full of grace and truth. Here, at last, was the one man who stood in utter, glorious integrity; a man without any contradictions. If we sometimes have difficulties with that, as when Jesus drives the money-changers from the Temple, or heals only one man at the Pool of Bethesda, or makes claims to Deity, or lashes the Pharisees with his tongue, it is only because we ourselves are so full of contradictions that we cannot imagine how to behave in his position. Jesus was utterly sure of himself because he was utterly pure.

'That is why he could throw down the gauntlet before the most critical judges of the day with the challenge, "Which of you convicts me of sin?" None rose to it. He was, as Peter said, "a lamb without blemish or spot".

'Nor was this simply an absence of evil. Jesus *loved* righteousness. It was his constant delight to please his Father. A wholeness which is not joyful is not the wholeness of Jesus. Though a man of sorrows in his identification with our sin and suffering, his life throbbed with the sheer delight of holy fellowship with God. People have been at pains in recent years to show that Jesus had a sense of humour. However true that may be, he is much more than just a nice guy. What he possessed was the deep, eternal joy of God which springs from utter righteousness and total union with the Father.'

Mr Christian warmed to his task: 'Can you imagine the leap of joy in Jesus' heart when, at his baptism, the Holy Spirit descended upon him and the Father cried, "You are my beloved Son, with you I am well pleased"? Or the sheer pleasure of long nights of prayer? Imagine having a heart with no reluctance to pray, no sins to confess, no uncertainty of acceptance, no doubt as to the will of God!

'Consider the wisdom which flowed from his lips. "No man ever spoke like this man!" the crowds cried in wonder. Living truth poured from his Spirit-touched lips to create hope, forgiveness and deliverance in the hearts of his hearers. Words to straighten out the tangle of misunderstanding, to unmask hypocrisy, to penetrate the heart. Words of such authority and boundless compassion that sinners never wanted to sin again, sick folk cast aside their crutches and begging bowls—even the dead sat up!

'When a disconsolate John the Baptist sent messengers to ask if Jesus really was the Messiah his reply was emphatic, "Go and tell John what you have seen: the blind receive their sight, the lame walk, lepers are cleansed, and the deaf hear, the dead are raised up, the poor have good news preached to them." Jesus' wholeness was no selfish matter; it ministered effectively to others. His health he passed on to the sick and needy people about him. This is what God's heart is like towards us. He yearns to touch our lives with the fullness of his Son so that we too might be made whole.

'It's no surprise, then, to find Jesus having authority over his environment. We see it, not in some arbitrary demonstration of power, but in the bringing in of the rule of God for the blessing of mankind. Healing the sick, feeding the five thousand, calming the storm, turning water into wine; these mighty acts of Jesus reveal the extent of spiritual authority which flows out of divine wholeness.

'The same is true when he confronts the dark forces. Demons flee powerless before him. When the ancient Prince of Darkness three times challenges Jesus' sonship in the wilderness, the story is the same. History is littered with broken messiahs whose inner unrighteousness could not handle this trinity of temptations. Not so Jesus! He will not yield to self-gratification, nor covet the world at any price, nor become a spiritual showbiz personality. Instead, he comes forth unscathed to do the Father's bidding in the full anointing of the Holy Spirit.

'But God doesn't simply send a whole man into the world to show up our inadequacies; he sent his Son to deal radically with our unrighteousness and with all its consequences. Jesus came to die as a willing substitute for us. The Bible says, "For our sake he made him to be sin who knew no sin, so that in him we might become the righteousness of God" (2 Corinthians 5:21). What this means, in the simplest terms, is that Jesus took all our guilt and sin and shame upon himself and suffered judgement for it, enduring hell on our behalf, in order that the slate could be wiped completely clean. That then freed us to come into all the benefits of his perfect life so that God would look upon us in the same way as he looks upon Jesus. That's why we can be called sons of God.

'More than six hundred years before this took place, Isaiah prophesied about Jesus: "Surely he has borne our sicknesses and carried our pains...he was wounded for our transgressions; he was bruised for our iniquities; upon him was the chastisement that made us *whole*, and with his stripes we are healed" (Isaiah 53:4–5).

'All our guilt is dealt with, all our sin atoned for. Jesus became ill for us so that we might be well, unrighteous to make us righteous, tormented to put us at peace, dead that we might live, alienated and rejected in order that we might know love and acceptance. The cross was vile and violent, a place of bloody torture and a vivid expression of the awful state of mankind; but it was also the greatest expression of the love and grace of God that the world has ever seen or will see.'

Mr Christian quoted from Ephesians 2:14–15: 'He is our

peace, who has made us both one, [estranged Jews and Gentiles] that he might create in himself one new man in place of the two, so making peace, and might reconcile us both to God in one body through the cross.' He pointed out that corporate as well as personal wholeness flows from the cross. It alone has the power to reconcile us to God, to ourselves and to one another.

Hence, all Christian wholeness must be cross-centred and Christ-centred. Anything which detracts from that must be judged to be of a false spirit, whatever pretentions it might have to spirituality. The fundamental key to the discerning of spirits lies in the question: what does this teaching or practice have to say concerning Christ? How does it accord with his character and teaching? What place is given to the work of the cross?

'But how many of us Christians limit the power of the cross,' Mr Christian continued passionately. ' "For in him all the fullness of God was pleased to dwell, and through him to reconcile to himself *all things*, whether on earth or in heaven, making peace by the blood of his cross" (Colossians 1:19–20). The fullness of Christ is to bring reconciliation and wholeness to every part of our lives. You can be forgiven through him, bodies can be healed, minds made new, fears broken, stresses relieved, enemies reconciled, bad habits destroyed, situations transformed. *All* things, my friends, *all* things. "For in him all the fullness of Deity dwells in bodily form, and in him you have been made complete" (Colossians 2:9–10 NASB). Many of us have got as far as believing that Jesus died for our sins, but will we not let him make us completely whole?

'I mentioned earlier the promise in Psalm 85 that righteousness and peace would meet. Jesus is the fulfilment of that promise. Hebrews 7 describes him as a Priest after the order of Melchizedek, the King of righteousness and peace. These virtues don't kiss in the abstract. They meet in a Person. As we reach out to him in our need, he himself will come to us and make us whole.

'Don't trust in vain alternatives. Put aside your unbelief. Let the power of his indestructible life touch every part of your being. Be made whole.'

'Glory!' cried the Pilgrim Watcher, as Mr Christian concluded.

*   *   *

Both the Courier and Susan had been much moved by what they had heard and came to see Mr Christian after lunch.

They found him sprawled in an armchair with his feet up—his normal after-preaching-and-Sunday-lunch posture, he explained. Zoë, his wife, excused herself after serving coffee saying she had to sort out a 'peasants' revolt' amongst the children over who should wash up and who dry.

Sunlight dappled its way through a filigree of leafy pot plants in the window bay and somewhere through the open casement a bee droned lazily. Peace reigned in the beige suburban lounge.

'I was glad you said wholeness begins in the soul, Peter,' began the Courier. 'At least, that's what I understood you to mean. And I agree with you. It seems to me that the great mistake materialists make is to blame all our troubles on the externals, on the environment, if you like. Lack of adequate housing, poor educational opportunities, racial and sexual discrimination and economic injustice—they've all been held responsible for the present mess by those who believe man's innate goodness will shine through if it's only given the opportunity. I don't believe that's true, even though my father lived through the horrors of the Depression.'

'But surely it's a good thing to improve our social conditions, don't you think?' asked Susan, who sat on the sofa next to him.

'Oh yes, indeed,' he replied. 'I believe we should do all we can to improve our lot, especially for the poor and deprived. But that by itself never works.'

'That's right,' agreed Mr Christian. 'I believe

environmental factors are important, too, and true wholeness radically affects our surroundings. But we mustn't put the cart before the horse; a healthy outer life flows from a healthy inner life. If we don't get the latter right we'll land up in cynicism and disillusionment, as many have today. But I must be honest, Christians have often put so much stress on the horse that they've forgotten the cart altogether. The challenge of biblical wholeness is that it affects everything, our total lifestyle gets renewed.'

Susan spoke seriously to Mr Christian. 'You challenged me very deeply this morning and I feel I've come a long way in a short time. You see, I'd been losing faith in Jesus. I never intended to but, well, it's just that Leo doesn't believe he's the Son of God. He says Jesus was a great teacher and a psychic—like many other religious figures in history—but nothing more. The cross, he says, isn't really that important, a noble sacrifice but that's all. And I guess I was beginning to believe him,' she ended lamely.

Mr Christian nodded sympathetically then explained that, in the end, all New Age Consciousness movements are syncretistic. Their adherents believe that all religions are like rivers flowing into one great sea of psychic awareness.

So pervasive is this teaching today that even some professing Christians are prepared to deny the exclusive claims of Christ and reinterpret the faith in the light of this all-embracing false creed. It is really the re-emergence of the second century Gnostic heresy—a mixture of Christianity with pagan philosophy, mysticism and occultism—which threatened to destroy the church in its prime by undermining the distinctiveness and uniqueness of the gospel. Once more it is necessary to stand firm on our confession concerning Jesus. He is God's only begotten eternal Son and salvation is found in no one else but him.

'Yes, I'm seeing that again, thank goodness,' said Susan. 'But I still have a problem, Peter, and it's to do with the church. Why is it that my church could do nothing for my back trouble and seemed not to care for me? Yet you say

Leo and his folk are not only misguided but motivated by demons, even though they showed me love and healed my back. I find that very confusing.'

'I think a lot of people feel that confusion,' agreed the Courier. 'They see the church criticizing these alternatives, perhaps rightly, but not coming up with anything better. What do you say to that, Peter?'

Mr Christian stroked his beard thoughtfully for a few moments before replying.

'I think it's to do with what I've been saying this morning. Many Christians haven't discovered wholeness for themselves and, therefore, don't know how to minister it to others. Sad to say, church is often little more than formal meetings of people who hardly know one another at all. It's what I call "snooker ball fellowship", lives touching briefly at the minimum point of contact. I've come across many lonely, hurt saints who are that way largely because they're in those kinds of churches. Other churches are full of bitterness and resentment, with gossip and criticism flying around and longstanding problems unresolved.'

'Why do you think that is?' asked the Courier, appreciating the other's candour.

'There are many reasons, Dai, but I would say the prime one is, again, *legalism*. There's nothing more guaranteed to produce a miserable, dead orthodoxy than that.'

When pressed to explain what he meant by legalism, Mr Christian said there are two meanings to the word. The first is salvation by works and this is the basis for most of the world religions, for the cults and for decadent Christendom. Be good, be decent, keep the rules, do your duty, serve the cause and you will be saved. Mr Aquarius' alternative is also a form of legalism in that it is motivated not by the grace of God but by humanistic self-effort.

The other meaning of the word has to do with an orthodox Christianity in which it is acknowledged that salvation is by grace but where a whole lot of extra traditions, rules and regulations actually govern the practice of the religion.

These might range from what one can or cannot do on a Sunday, how church services should be conducted or the length of daily devotions, through to what foods are permitted or banned. In fact, the rules can cover anything, because legalism is an attitude of heart rather than any particular practice.

Paul deals with the whole subject in his Galatian letter and has no hesitation about calling this 'faith-plus-works' teaching another gospel and one which is motivated by 'weak and beggarly elemental spirits'. He warns his readers in the strongest possible terms to have nothing to do with such a message.

'You mean you're saying that the same spirits which are at work in Leo's commune can also be in the church?' gasped Susan.

'I'm afraid so. In fact, Paul wrote to Timothy that some would "Depart from the faith by giving heed to deceitful spirits and doctrines of demons, through the pretensions of liars whose consciences are seared, who forbid marriage and enjoin abstinence from foods which God created to be received with thanksgiving..."' (1 Timothy 4:1–3).

'Phew, that's strong language!' declared the Courier.

'Yes, but the issues are so vital. Legalism, in any form, undermines what Jesus did on the cross and reduces our dependence upon him. A nice little rule is a tempting substitute for personal guidance,' said Mr Christian. 'Then people get locked into a vicious circle of striving, failure, guilt and depression. The work of the Holy Spirit is quenched so they live a powerless, joyless and fruitless sort of Christianity which doesn't deeply transform either them or the world about them. That in turn leads to all sorts of bitternesses and hang-ups, as well as physical ailments of one kind and another.'

'That makes a lot of sense of the church I've been attending,' said Susan. 'I can see that people know the truth but are in some kind of spiritual straightjacket all the time. That's why Leo's people seemed to me to be so much better. I think I can see now that they're not, but they did appear to have something my church lacked.'

The Courier said he thought Mr Christian's church was not like that and wanted to know what the difference was. Mr Christian pondered for a moment then smiled. 'Let me give you an illustration of what the difference is. Jenny Good was married to the wrong man. He was harsh, critical and violent. "Get my breakfast, you worthless wretch," he'd bellow at break of day. "And don't burn the toast like you did yesterday." Down the stairs he'd stomp, scowling all the way. "You stupid woman. My egg's overdone again. How many times do I have to drum it into your thick head? It's two minutes, forty-eight seconds for size three eggs. I really don't know why I put up with you!"

'By now Jenny was in tears. "I try, really I do. I know I'm not much good, but I do my best. You make me feel such a failure," she blubbered.

'Her husband appeared to soften for a moment. "Look, crying won't help, will it? Try harder next time. And you can work off your sense of failure by doing the house right through whilst I'm at work. Okay? The list's on the wall." Jenny nodded meekly. She was already dreading his return that night.

'Life continued for years in this vein until it took its inevitable toll and Jenny died. Her husband shrugged his shoulders regretfully. "I did my best for her, but she just wouldn't learn. Don't think she had it in her." '

'Poor Jenny!' Susan exclaimed.

'Then a miracle occurred,' Mr Christian continued. 'Jenny was raised from the dead. Of course, having died she was freed from her marriage vows and able to contemplate remarriage. No way was she going back to that old tyrant! Her days of slavery were over. And sure enough, before long, a kind, generous and encouraging man took her as his wife.

'Life was so different for Jenny; this man truly loved her. She didn't need to learn how to please him because he was already delighted in her for her own sake. When she made mistakes they laughed together. Where he could, he gently taught her how to do some things better and he never lost patience with her. She loved to serve him and blossomed ever more radiantly in his presence; her self-confidence grew daily as she discovered her new identity in relation to him. Her creative gifts were unlocked and he praised the work of her hands and extolled her virtues wherever he went. Jenny became a whole person.'

'That sounds wonderful,' said Susan, a little wistfully. 'What does it mean?'

He replied that it illustrates the difference between serving the Law and serving the Lord. Paul wrote about it in Romans 7:4–6, 'You have died to the law through the body of Christ, so that you may belong to another, to him who has been raised from the dead in order that we may bear fruit for God...we are discharged from the law, dead to that which held us captive, so that we serve not under the old written code but in the new life of the Spirit.'

He went on: 'Legalism keeps people in slavery. It destroys their self-worth. It produces condemnation and death. Those who succeed become proud, those who fail become pathetic. The good news of Jesus Christ is that we can utterly die to the Law and be completely released from its demands. This is what happens when we put our faith in Jesus. Though he had no need to, he came and lived under the Law, fulfilling both its letter and its spirit.

'Not only that, he died and took the curse of the Law upon himself for our sakes; he divested it of its power to accuse so that everyone who is "in Christ" is set free. A greater power has operated. "There is therefore now no condemnation for those who are in Christ Jesus. For the law of the Spirit of life in Christ Jesus has set me free from the law of sin and death"' (Romans 8:1–2).

'Explain that bit about the Spirit, Peter?' the Courier requested.

'Sure,' replied Mr Christian. 'Not only is the believer

now married to Christ in the New Covenant but he serves in a different way. You see, it's not that we become spiritual anarchists who feel free to sin as they like. Instead, God writes his laws on our hearts and motivates us to keep them *from within* in the power of the Holy Spirit. I don't steal because I no longer *want* to steal. God's word has become my word too.

'Let me quote you Paul's simple key to holy, non-legalistic living. It's in Galatians 5:16, "Walk by the Spirit, and you will not carry out the desire of the flesh"(NASB). Simple, isn't it?'

Susan said she had never been taught this before and could now understand why her life had been so uptight. Although she had given her heart to the Lord some years before, it had always seemed a hard uphill struggle to live the Christian life and at times her Christian faith had seemed to increase rather than lessen her problems. Many of the experiences of the New Testament believers had appeared hopelessly beyond her reach.

'How do I learn to live without legalism?' she asked.

Mr Christian suggested that she needed to be baptized in the Holy Spirit in order to enter the realm of spiritual freedom. Many believers never experience the power of the Holy Spirit simply because they have not been taught that they can. Faith comes by hearing the word of God. When Peter preached the promise of the Spirit on the Day of Pentecost his hearers received it and knew they had received it; they responded to the truth. All Susan needed to do was to cease striving and ask the Holy Spirit to come upon her so that she could live by his power to the glory of Jesus.

'Imagine you're in a boat trying to get across an expanse of water to the harbour,' he said. 'The wind is blowing, mostly in your favour, though a little gustily at times. What do you do? Many Christians get the oars out and row for all their might. That's what it's like when you aren't filled with the Spirit. It becomes really hard work. What God wants us to do—and this is how the Spirit-filled believer lives—is to raise the sail and catch the wind. Now that frees us from striving and leaves us just with the responsibility of making sure the sail is well-adjusted to the direction of the wind. It's a different style of living altogether. But it's what made the New Testament believers such a powerful and victorious people.'

Susan nodded.

'Are you saying then that Spirit-filled Christians are free from legalism?' the Courier asked. 'And what about those who aren't? Are they true believers?'

'I'll answer your second question first, if I may,' smiled Mr Christian. 'Yes, they're true believers all right but somehow are living subnormal Christian lives. I don't mean that at all unkindly or judgementally. It saddens me to see believers not experiencing the fullness of the gospel. I yearn for the day when all God's people will be truly on fire with the Holy Spirit and once more turn the world upside down.

'But to answer your first question, I'd say Spirit-filled believers are free but not without danger. Satan is for ever seeking new ways of bringing God's people into bondage. Someone once said, "The price of liberty is eternal vigilance;" we have to keep alert at all times to the danger. The ghost of Jenny's husband stalks about looking for someone to intimidate. I don't want to be that person!'

'Because of this danger,' he continued, 'it's very important not only to keep our own lives full of the Spirit and free from striving but also to purge the corporate life of the church from legalism. Institutional legalism is like a straightjacket around the work of the Spirit. That is why some believers, though Spirit-filled, have not been able to grow into wholeness.'

However godly an individual might be, no one person is ever going to contain the totality of Christ. That belongs to the church. Paul spoke of "building up the body of Christ, until we all attain to the unity of the faith and of the knowledge of the Son of God, to mature manhood, to the measure of the stature of the fullness of Christ" (Ephesians

4:12–13). The church which is going to be like this is one in which the Holy Spirit is not quenched by the traditions of men nor motivated by a heavy sense of duty but instead is flexibly structured, consciously dependent upon the Lord at every step and experiencing the living manifestation of the Spirit. It is an open community of joyful, loving and deeply caring people.

'This is no ideal,' he continued. 'It's normal New Testament church life. Praise God, it's beginning to appear across the world again. God's answer to this world's needs is an alternative society of people made whole through their union with Christ and living in true health—I mean that in the broadest sense—by the power of the Holy Spirit. It's the most thrilling challenge of the century!'

'I want to be in that,' said Susan.

'I think I do too,' added the Courier.

*   *   *

That night Susan got down on her knees and prayed to be baptized in the Holy Spirit. She received a most glorious experience of love and acceptance which had her alternately laughing and sobbing. She spoke in tongues—the spiritual gift described in 1 Corinthians chapter 14—and spent until the small hours of the morning praising God with a liberty she had never before experienced. Years of struggling seemed to fall away and doubt fled from her like the shadow of a dream in the light of a new day. She was so excited she could hardly sleep but when she did it was sweet.

The Courier prayed too. And nothing happened. He was deeply disappointed but resolved to meet with Mr Christian the next day to talk about his problems. The Pilgrim Watcher let him know that he, too, would be there.

CHAPTER FIVE

Getting it Together

Oxford Street is an amazing road to walk along, not so much for its being one of the world's great shopping centres but because you can walk the mile and a quarter or so of its length and pass literally thousands upon thousands of people without actually touching or speaking to anybody. And everyone is doing the same; crowds upon crowds of lonely people insulated from one another for fear of any contact, any word, which might somehow get them *involved*. Such is the alienation which city life produces.

The Courier, Mr Christian and the Pilgrim Watcher made this journey and came at length to Marble Arch. From there they escaped into the quietness of Hyde Park and found a place to sit which overlooked the Serpentine. The Courier was glum.

'I prayed for the Holy Spirit last night,' he said. 'And nothing happened. To be perfectly frank I feel very disappointed and discouraged. I really thought I was getting somewhere yesterday but it seems it isn't going to happen to me.'

Mr Christian nodded understandingly. 'What did you feel as you began to pray?' he asked.

'Well, I started off all right,' the other replied. 'But then, all of a sudden, I felt empty inside, kind of lonely and useless, you know. I felt I was unwanted. Then I began to feel sorry for myself, so I gave up and…well…'

'…and turned to the bottle,' Mr Christian finished for him.

He assented gloomily.

It was at times like this that the Pilgrim Watcher was glad he was not of the race of men. How they suffered for being human! But then again, he reflected, they can know a joy infinitely greater than that of the Celestials. If only they would, though!

'Dai, let me tell you a story which may help,' Mr Christian suggested. He looked at his friend. 'It's about a very insecure lad I once knew. He couldn't say whether his parents had ever cuddled him or not. Certainly any show of physical affection he saw filled him with embarrassment; it wasn't something with which he could identify. He came from a poor family in a poor part of London. All his clothes were secondhand, ill-fitted and inadequate. It made him the butt of many a nasty joke; "scruff" they called him. He had no friends, his parents had no friends; he was a deeply lonely boy, born unto melancholy, the odd one out.

'Imagine him on one particular day. He's not long turned nine years of age. It's a bitter winter; a bitingly cold wind howls across frozen pavements, round snow-strewn corners, freezing his poorly covered ribs and bare knees. The sky is grey as iron as this hard-fisted weather smashes into his stomach. He has a gastric chill. And there he is, doubled up in agony, lying on the ice against a wall in the school playground. The cold and the pain tear at his inside and he's sobbing his little heart out. But nobody cares, no one comes to his aid, not one person responds to the cry of a desolate and rejected soul. So he's left to suffer and to bear his lonely wounds as best he can.'

Mr Christian saw from the movement in the Courier's sensitive features that he was touching upon reality in his life. He continued.

'Long years passed and the boy grew up. He became a

believer and served God with all his heart. But the wounds remained; rejection would grip him from time to time and plunge him into despair. He was always unsure of himself and uncertain about how people would receive him. At times it bordered upon catastrophe.

'Then one day the Lord graciously confronted him with his past pains. So raw were the unhealed wounds, so vicious the satanic grip, that he couldn't face them without deep anguish and tears. In a vision, he was returned to the school playground. Nothing was changed, history remained as cruel as it ever had been—but for this one thing. In his vision, he saw the Lord Jesus himself come across to that little boy and reach out his hand to touch him. Gently, he smiled into the lad's face and, in a moment, healed him completely. Then he took his hand and lifted him to his feet. He spoke with fatherly love and authority, "Come on, son, let's leave here and walk together, shall we?" The boy smiled gratefully (he had not often smiled) and, hand in hand, they departed. The pain and the loneliness were over. He knew he was *wanted* for the first time in his life.

'For the grown man, history telescoped. No longer did he refuse to be comforted out of hurt self-pity. The Lord delivered him from his rejection and healed his wounds; God himself brought wholeness to his inner being as the weight of the years fell away. Peace and security and a lightness of soul became his at long last.'

'Who was that man?' asked the Courier, whose eyes were brimming with tears.

'That little boy was me,' Mr Christian replied quietly. 'I am the one the Lord healed.' He could scarce restrain a tear himself as he recalled the Lord's kindness towards him.

'Hallelujah!' breathed the Pilgrim Watcher.

The Courier shook his head slowly. 'It could have been me. The details are different, but it could have been me. Or so many others I've met,' he added. 'Why is it such vast numbers of us are hurt and rejected like this? Can you tell me that, man?' He spoke fiercely.

'It's an age of rejection,' Mr Christian replied. 'I sometimes think the Second World War had a lot to do with it. Those terrible years scarred so many people as they saw the horrors of hatred, as they did the unthinkable and as they lost their loved ones.

'Feelings become frozen at such times. The wounds flesh over but the poison remains, eating into the vitals. The offspring of that generation inherited the same disease. So often their parents couldn't give them what they needed. So they've grown up unstable themselves. You see that in the way their marriages shatter and their children undergo the same experiences of rejection. Truly iniquity is visited to the third and fourth generation of those who hate God! Satan will keep this going as long as possible because the spirit of rejection is an open door to all other kinds of bondage.'

He described rejection as a black hole in the centre of the personality, a voracious devil, devouring the soul, feeding on hurt, self-pity and fear. Trying to cope with this gnawing ache leads some to rebellion and violence, others to despair, anxiety and self-comfort. For many, life is a see-saw of conflicting emotions and, when they are extreme, schizophrenia sometimes develops and the personality becomes utterly fragmented.

'I want to be free,' cried the Courier earnestly. 'This is what I'm like, Peter. I'm some kind of Welsh depressionist, painting bleak pictures in my mind which mirror my desolate soul. I fight society. I'm lonely and I feel unwanted. What must I do to be delivered from this?'

In answer, Mr Christian spoke no obscure word of secret knowledge. What he said was simple, and applies to so many broken lives. He just said, 'Forgive your parents from the heart. And anybody else whom you feel has hurt you.'

The sword thrust home.

'I don't know that I can. It's so very hard to go over the past like that. Is it really essential?'

Mr Christian opened his Bible and turned to Matthew

18:23–25 where the parable of the unforgiving servant is recorded. He drew the Courier's attention to the Lord's judgement on the one who would not forgive. "And in anger his lord delivered him to the torturers, till he should pay all his debt. So also my heavenly Father will do to every one of you, if you do not forgive your brother from your heart" (verses 34–35).

'Unforgiveness gives continual ground for the devil to torment our lives,' he explained. 'It leaves us exposed to judgement. That's why Jesus taught us to pray, "Forgive us our trespasses as we forgive those who trespass against us." You can see it in the way you suffer, and how I once suffered. Our souls remain sore until we express forgiveness to those who first caused the pain. I'm convinced many people are in mental hospitals for this reason alone—they just will not forgive.

'Some of those torturers can affect the body too,' he went on. 'Unforgiveness produces resentment, bitterness, anger and hatred. These negative emotions cause chemical changes in the body which help produce diseases such as arthritis, stomach ulcers, colitis, high blood pressure, asthma, even sudden death. The inner conflicts caused by resentment lead to fatigue and tension, and that in itself leaves people vulnerable to sicknesses of one kind or another. One of the Proverbs puts it like this, "A tranquil mind gives life to the flesh, but passion makes the bones rot" (Proverbs 14:30). Forgiveness is one of the first steps into health.'

The Courier was impressed by the sense in what Mr Christian was saying but obviously had difficulty with actually doing it. His hurts and resentments went deep. He realized that it would need a decision, an act of the will, to forgive those who had wounded him. Sensing that this was not the time or the place for this to happen, Mr Christian changed tack.

'Rejection is obviously the cause of the feelings you experienced when you tried to pray last night, Dai, and that has roots in your past. But God can touch all that and release you from those hang-ups. The reason it's possible is because Jesus himself has suffered rejection.'

The Courier looked up at him. 'Go on.'

'Do you remember those strange, desolate words Jesus cried on the cross? "My God, my God, why have you forsaken me?" In that moment Jesus bore our alienation. As he took our sins he experienced separation from the Father himself. I confess it's a mystery too deep to understand; but it's true. Jesus knew the pain of rejection so that we might be healed from it and find eternal acceptance.'

'If you'll believe it and put your faith in the power of the cross, I'm sure you'll find it possible to exercise forgiveness and be released from the Enemy's grip.'

'Look, I haven't faced that yet, Peter, and I will take you seriously. But I think I'd better say that this isn't the first time I've tried to get rid of these feelings,' the Courier replied. 'Several years ago I went away on a course I'd seen advertised and it turned out to be on Primal Scream Therapy.'

The Pilgrim Watcher, who had been listening quietly, confessed that this was new to him and asked for an explanation. Between them they tried to sum up the theory which a writer named Janov had proposed.

His fundamental thesis is that experiences of a harmful or hurtful nature which are undergone by the embryo, foetus, infant or child, create a pool of Primal Pain in the personality. It is this which is the source of neurosis and split personality. In general, people seek to suppress this pain by means of tranquillizers and social insulators of one kind or another. Janov's treatment begins with a three week period of isolation from all these means of avoiding or suppressing the pain. This involves separation from work, family, comforts and drugs. There follows a nine month period during which the patient goes into his own pain and allows himself to feel it. As he does so, he discharges it by sobbing and screaming.

The course which the Courier had been on had not been

conducted by Janov but was, rather, a crash course in Primal Therapy. The isolation and confrontation techniques had quickly uncovered his wounds and the attempts to scream out the pain had been traumatic in the extreme. It had frightened him, in spite of reassurances that all was well. He had not been healed.

'I feel Janov is on the right lines when he recognizes the reality of hurts in early life,' said Mr Christian. 'However, I'd put much of this down to the work of malignant spirits which need casting out. As far as I can see, Primal Therapy effectively seeks to be a form of assisted self-deliverance but without reference to the power of Christ or the cross. It's a risky operation to put it mildly!'

The New Testament is quite unapologetic about the existence of demons. Both Jesus and the apostles cast many evil spirits out of people and indeed it was a sign of the advent of the kingdom of God that this should be so. The Scriptures do not greatly differentiate between demonic 'oppression' and 'possession'; the most commonly used term is best translated 'demonized'. Manifestations are diverse; sometimes demonization reveals itself in sickness, sometimes in psychiatric problems, occasionally in violently aberrant behaviour. The common factor is a bondage which is discerned to be more than simply a human problem.

Two extremes are to be avoided. On the one hand, it will not do to write off demons on the specious ground that Jesus knew no better! Not all problems are simply psychiatric or medical. At the same time, we must beware of attributing every difficulty to a demonic manifestation. The Scriptures do not make this mistake but, rather, hold us personally responsible for our behaviour patterns. Hence the stress upon the renewal of the mind and living by the Spirit. It requires the spiritual gift of discernment to properly diagnose the source of a problem.

The casting out of demons is a greatly abused ministry. At the two extremes there are those who make it a dramatic public display and those who perform a symbolic, sacerdotal

rite. In neither case is a demon necessarily cast out. True
deliverance is best accomplished as privately as is reasonable. It does not depend upon any particular technique but
is effected simply by the power of the Holy Spirit and in the
authoritative name of Jesus. The context must be one of
love and security. There will be positive evidence of release.

This is followed, not by months of painful regression, but
by encouragement to be filled with the Spirit and to renew
the mind and behaviour patterns by means of the Scriptures.

Later that day the Courier received ministry which
tackled his inner fragmentation. Some things were painful
to face, but he was gloriously released. The lordship of
Christ became a reality to him for the first time in his life as
he experienced his living authority over the powers of
darkness. This time, as hands were laid upon him, he had
no difficulty in receiving the Holy Spirit. The peace and
fullness of God washed through his entire being. He felt the
love of the Father and knew he was eternally accepted as a
child of God. Life was going to be different from now on!

*   *   *

'I have been spying,' said the Pilgrim Watcher conspir-
atorially.

Mr Christian looked up from his book in surprise. It had
been several days since he had seen any of his companions
and he had been very busy on other things. The Pilgrim
Watcher had just disconcertingly materialized in the
armchair opposite him.

'Oh, hello. I was wondering where you'd got to. So, who
have you been spying on? Not me, I hope!'

'No, not you,' the Pilgrim Watcher replied. 'Though
why should you have cause for worry? Besides, you believers
are watched all the time.'

Before Mr Christian could make an appropriate rejoinder,
he continued, 'I have been observing a Christian husband
and wife named Tim and Jane and I think I may have done

them some good. They have been in a most sorry state. They have been married for these five years, and with great diligence they work in their church, but in their own home their life together is terrible to behold!'

When Mr Christian asked him to explain what he meant, the Pilgrim Watcher gave his observations.

'It is plain to see that they love each other and their marriage is in the will of the Father, but they will not refrain from hurting one another. It begins at the start of each morning. Both of them go out to work and they are in a great hurry. They have little discourse together and what they say consists of complaining and grumbling. Tim grumbles that he cannot find his papers; Jane complains that he does not assist around the house. Especially are they in error in their use of the words "always" and "never". They say, "You're *always* moving my things." "You *never* give me a hand." By that means they turn trifling issues into a way of life. Then they begin to believe this twisted confession.'

He went on to say they were even more irritable with each other after a hard day's work. Sometimes they became quite angry and quarrelsome. That was where the difficulties really began, because Jane was articulate and well knew how to demean her husband. He reacted with verbal abuse. They then retreated into silent, self-righteous sulking for the rest of the evening.

'Do they put things right before they go to sleep?' asked Mr Christian.

'No, most often they turn over and have what I have heard some of your teachers call "back to back fellowship". They have built up a pile of problems but they have no discourse about them. Thus when they make love the reconciliation is the least necessary to give them some slight pleasure.'

'My wife and I have made quite a few mistakes in our marriage,' Mr Christian confessed. 'But one simple key has got us through them all and it's what Paul wrote to the

Ephesians, "Be angry but do not sin; do not let the sun go down on your anger, and give no opportunity to the devil" (Ephesians 4:26–27). You can't have a deep relationship without disagreements on occasions but they should never be allowed to outlast the day. There have been times when we've tried to go to sleep unreconciled, but we just can't do it! We lie there tossing and turning until we put it right!'

'Who is the first to make peace?' asked the Pilgrim Watcher.

'Oh, I believe it's the husband's responsibility to say sorry first, even if it wasn't his fault in the beginning! That's part of what it means to lay down his life for his wife. You see, she's the weaker vessel and is far more threatened by rows and upsets than he is. That makes it harder for her to respond.'

'It does my heart good to hear you say that,' the Pilgrim Watcher replied. 'This is something that Tim does not believe. He thinks to himself that his wife is stronger than he. He fears her strength and speaks with anger to her to protect himself. Then she also is full of fear and insecurity.'

'That sort of attitude seeks to divide what God has joined together,' said Mr Christian. 'It really is giving an opportunity to the devil. The Lord intended Christian marriage to be an expression of wholeness so that a couple who are "joint-heirs of the grace of life" should be in the same loving unity as are Christ and the church.'

The Pilgrim Watcher smiled.

'Well, that is the very scripture I brought before them, from 1 Peter 3. I should not do this too often, but I made their Bible fall open at this passage and persuaded them to read it together.' He quoted from memory. ' "For after this manner in the old time the holy women also, who trusted in God, adorned themselves, being in subjection unto their own husbands: Even as Sarah obeyed Abraham, calling him lord: whose daughters ye are, as long as ye do well, and are not afraid with any amazement. Likewise, ye husbands, dwell with them according to knowledge, giving honour unto the wife, as unto the weaker vessel."

'They both feel threatened by each other,' he explained. 'Jane has need of hope in God. She has need to believe the Lord will keep her safe as she submits herself to Tim, though oftentimes he makes a mess of things. After all, I well remember the mistakes Abraham made. We were directly involved in putting that to rights, I recall.'

'But that's the whole point, isn't it?' Mr Christian agreed. 'The Lord is with us and honours our obedience to his word, in spite of our human shortcomings.'

He nodded. 'Yes, and Tim must needs believe the truth about how God has made his wife. He looks at his wife from the outside and sees that she is most capable. He fails to perceive what she is like on the inside. If he would see her as truly weaker, he would not feel threatened, neither would he attack her so.

'But now, they are beginning to understand. They have had an honest time together and have prayed much for each other. I think there is hope for wholeness in their relationship.'

Mr Christian was delighted to hear it. Unhealthy marriages cause illness, he thought. One cannot enter such a deep commitment without becoming vulnerable and when things go wrong it has a very profound effect upon personal well-being.

'I remember a woman in her late fifties speaking to my wife on one occasion,' Mr Christian said. 'She spoke very disparagingly about her husband and when she referred to their sex life, she declared, "I soon put a stop to that nonsense!" I wasn't really surprised to hear that he recently underwent surgery on his prostate gland. Perhaps that's the kind of thing Solomon had in mind when he wrote, "A good wife is the crown of her husband, but she who brings shame is like rottenness in his bones" (Proverbs 12:4).

Mr Christian said that marriage has been very much under attack in recent years and one of the tremendous testimonies of the renewed church is its superbly successful marriage record. So many broken and brittle relationships have been made whole, so many children saved from rejection. Divorce is virtually unknown amongst those who walk with God.

'Our church family is breaking bread tonight. Are you coming?' Mr Christian asked the Pilgrim Watcher.

'I am indeed. To celebrate the Lamb's victory is my chief delight. I will be there. Farewell, until then.'

And with that he vanished.

*   *   *

Mr Christian met the Courier at the station. The latter was looking much more cheerful and smiled a warm greeting. As they set off to walk the mile to the meeting hall he enthused over the blessings of the past few days. Then he said, 'I wonder if I could ask you a question? There's something I've noticed in your church which is very different to the chapel I was forced to attend as a child back in Wales. You all hug one another. It doesn't seem, well, very British, if you understand me. Not that I'm complaining, mind,' he added hastily. 'But it shook me a bit at first, I must confess.'

Mr Christian laughed.

'I agree, it's not very British, at least, if you discount the football pitch. (To which the Courier chipped in that he always discounted football; he much preferred rugby!) But, you see, there are things in all cultures which are distinctly harmful and make for alienation. In Britain one of these is our reserve, our lack of physical contact and our embarrassment at displays of emotion. It's given us a world-wide reputation for *sang-froid*. But it's not at all healthy.'

He went on to say that people need physical contact of a non-sexual kind. Babies deprived of maternal and paternal cuddling grow up tense, wary, and rejected. It is not so much that "breast is best", though that is true, but that prolonged skin to skin contact is essential for a baby's well-being, even if bottle feeding proves necessary. Children need hugging and plenty of "bundles" with their parents.

And teenagers can be greatly helped through their physically self-conscious years by pure physical contact with their parents. Many teenagers fall prey to lust simply for lack of somebody to hold them tight. Many adults today have experienced serious physical deprivation and inwardly long for such contact, but have become afraid of it.

'I remember years ago, before hugging was commonplace in churches, visiting a fellowship in East London where they had an epileptic man. They'd discovered that whenever he began to go into a fit, all that was needed for it to pass was for one of the members to put their arms gently around him. Now obviously that isn't the answer to all cases of epilepsy, but it does illustrate the power of loving touch.'

The Courier was impressed, so Mr Christian continued, 'Imagine the effect upon the man with leprosy when Jesus reached out and touched him. For years he'd been shunned by everybody. The law required him to ring a bell and cry "unclean" whenever he drew near to people. He must have been very lonely and yearned for human contact. Then Jesus touches him. A moment later he's healed. Powerful stuff this laying on of hands! That's why we do it when we pray for the sick, you know; we're showing God's compassion and being a physical channel of the Holy Spirit's healing power to the needy person.

'True Christianity,' he said, 'really is the most earthy and physical of all the world religions. That's why it gives sterile intellectuals such problems. They want to "purify" it of its so-called crudities. But God just won't have it!'

'I can see that the power of touch is very important,' the Courier replied. 'Part of being made whole is going to be the ability to cross the insulation barrier we put around ourselves, if you understand what I mean. Actually, I spoke with Leo about this the other day. Now I don't know what you'll think, but he said all objects are surrounded by a kind of bright aura, blue-grey around humans, which some can see and which can be recorded by means of high-voltage photography. Breaks in the aura indicate disease.'

'Yes,' Mr Christian answered. 'He'd claim this as evidence for man's psychic nature. To be honest, it's an uncertain area. Scientific research on the subject is inconclusive, but in the end may show no more than that people give off some form of electrical discharge which can be detected by sensitive individuals. Personally, I don't need that evidence to prove I'm more than just a machine. The fact that the aura can be interpreted as a merely physical phenomenon, a bit like the Aurora Borealis, doesn't help the case at all. My conviction that humans have a spirit is based upon my knowledge of God himself, who is Spirit, and in whose image we're made. Anyhow, what's that to do with touching people?'

'Oh, touch therapies, you know. He says the healing aura around him can be ministered to someone else by, say, massage.'

'Yes,' said Mr Christian, 'I know that there are a number of these touch therapies. Some involve total body massage; others concentrate on a part of the body, such as the feet or the scalp. Shiatsu massage is a Japanese method based on the theory that there are trigger points just under the skin. These follow definite lines called meridians and stimulation of these meridians helps various organs to function better. It's a kind of needle-less form of acupuncture. Then there are those contact therapies which seek to break down psychological inhibitions. Many of these are exercised in group contexts and some include overt sexual contact.'

'What do you think of all this, then?' asked the Courier. 'Does it do any harm?'

'Well,' said Mr Christian. 'There's nothing wrong with physical massage performed as a proper form of physiotherapy for the relaxation and manipulation of muscles. Though there are, of course, "massage parlours" and "relaxing massage" advertisements in some newspapers which are just another name for prostitution, and we'd better steer clear of those. Nor can I see anything wrong with a qualified osteopath or chiropractic manipulating joints. These are generally nothing more than physical adjustments.'

His big caution, however, was that increasingly alternative medicine practitioners are "finding" one another nowadays and the psychic aspects are coming more to the fore. What Mr Aquarius is doing is spiritually dangerous for, although he claims only to be drawing on his own resources or the Ultimate Life Force, by so doing he is actually opening himself to being a channel for demonic activity.

'Hm, I can see what you're saying,' said the Courier. 'But surely it would be all right for you, say, to practise these things because you'd be relying on the Holy Spirit for the healing? After all, you already lay on hands to heal the sick. Couldn't this be developed into a ministry of Holy Spirit massage?'

'Yes, in theory it could, I suppose,' Mr Christian answered cautiously. 'And there are occasions when I've, for example, been praying for somebody with migraine and at the same time massaged their tense neck muscles. Actually, tense necks are not uncommon in our family and we often give each other a massage at the end of a busy day. But I think the danger in your suggestion is that we'll become dependent upon the means rather than upon the Holy Spirit himself for healing.

'Novel techniques are often attractive to people who want an alternative to conventional pain-killer medicine. Personally I feel we need to go to the Lord for healing and let him direct us in each specific case and show us if he wishes us to use some physical means as well. That appears to have been Jesus' way.

'Either way, I want to avoid the mystical approach of Mr Aquarius and I would advise anyone seeking touch therapy to exercise the utmost caution and to avoid any practitioner who is associated with New Age Consciousness and keep away even from professing Christians where there's the least question about them.'

By now they had arrived at the meeting place.

'Well,' laughed Mr Christian, 'we seem to have come quite a way from one simple Christian expression of love. By the way, it's in the Scriptures, you know, "Greet one another with a holy kiss" (1 Corinthians 16:20).'

Susan was standing at the door wearing a light blue dress and looking quite radiant. The Courier hastened across to her. He would have given her a hug but was suddenly unsure of himself. He thought he felt more for her than if she were just another Christian but he didn't yet know how she would respond. He spoke shyly.

'Hallo, Susan. Er...um, I'm glad you could come.'

She looked at him demurely from beneath her long lashes.

'Hallo, Dai. I'm glad you could too. I've been so blessed, I really wanted to tell you.'

'So have I,' he replied. 'I'd love to tell you all about it, too.'

'Well let's go inside and I'll tell you what's been happening to me and you tell me your story.'

They laughed, and agreed. Their shyness was over and they entered together.

*   *   *

The Lord's Supper is for many little more than a memory jogger, a mental re-enactment of the crucifixion which, though undoubtably touching the heart strings, does little to affect life or health or relationships. This is a far cry from the covenant commitment which the early believers had towards one another as they devoted themselves to "the apostles' teaching and to fellowship, to the breaking of bread and to prayer" and so came to see that oneness with Jesus meant oneness with each other also. Paul writes, "The cup of blessing which we bless, is it not a participation in the blood of Christ? The bread which we break, is it not a participation in the body of Christ? Because there is one bread, we who are many are one body, for we all partake of the one bread" (1 Corinthians 10:16-17).

It is not possible, therefore, to celebrate the Lord's Supper in isolation. By its very nature it is a fellowship meal. Hence, whether it is held around a family table or in a great congregation, its format should allow realistic expression of that fellowship and the opportunity to remedy any defects. The table is a place of healing.

Before this congregation shared the bread and wine a young man called Jim stood up to share some thoughts.

'I feel God wants to do us good tonight,' he began. 'Especially in the realm of healing. You know, the cross is the place where we find peace and wholeness. We were reminded of that the other day when we looked at Ephesians 2 and saw that Jesus reconciles us to God and to each other through his death. So I just want to share a couple of things, if I may.

'The first is that we've been brought into oneness with the Father. We have fellowship with God. It's not something for which we've got to strive but something to enjoy. Just think, by the Holy Spirit, we're permanently connected up to the Creator of the universe. We've got constant access to the very throne of God. I wonder if you felt that when you were on the train this morning? Or when you were doing the washing up?'

A few folk laughed. They hadn't really experienced that.

'I want to be honest,' Jim continued. 'I've had a lousy day. Everything seems to have gone wrong. I got stuck in a traffic jam, so I was late for work. And guess who walked straight into the boss! I couldn't find half the files I needed. The telephone never stopped ringing all day. I tell you, by the end of the afternoon I was really screwed up and I'd nearly forgotten that God existed, let alone that he was with me. Anyone else ever felt like that?'

Quite a number nodded sympathetically.

'Well, it's a false feeling, because he's there all the time whether we feel it or not. But I want to *experience* that more and more each day. Anyway, even if you've had a day like mine, tonight we can feed on Christ, we can share his life afresh and find healing and encouragement. See, the bread and wine are not just symbols. If we take them in faith they become a means whereby we experience deep communion with the Lord, and he'll minister his wholeness to us afresh.

'The other thing I want to say is that we can find healing in our relationships around this table.'

Jim read Paul's well-known words to the Corinthians: "Let a man examine himself, and so eat of the bread and drink of the cup. For anyone who eats and drinks without discerning the body eats and drinks judgement upon himself. That is why many of you are weak and ill, and some have fallen asleep. But if we judged ourselves truly, we should not be judged" (1 Corinthians 11:28–31).

'These are serious words. They tell us that if we're out of fellowship with one another at this place of covenant cele-bration, we get sick and may even die. I don't think it's simply cause and effect but God's discipline to remind us how important our fellowship is.

'I just want to ask that we check whether we've got anything to put right with each other. Any resentments to put away. Any apologies to make. Now we could apply this to lots of areas but I feel the Lord is telling me to emphasize the matter of our speech. How do we use our tongues? So I want to read a couple of Proverbs and then some words from Ephesians.

'Proverbs 12:18 says: "There is one whose rash words are like sword thrusts, but the tongue of the wise brings healing." And chapter 16:24 adds: "Pleasant words are like a honey-comb, sweetness to the soul and health to the body."

'There is no greater untruth than the schoolboy's catcall, "Sticks and stones may break my bones, but words can't hurt me!" Words can kill. But they can also heal. This is why Paul instructed the Ephesians, "Let no evil talk come out of your mouths, but only such as is good for edifying, as fits the occasion, that it may impart grace to those who hear." (Ephesians 4:29). He went on to condemn those evil heart attitudes which give rise to slander and gossip. Instead, we are to be kind, tender-hearted and forgiving—because that's the way the Lord has treated us.

'God wants us to have a lovely positive attitude towards each other. The Hollies recorded a song once with the title, "He's not heavy, he's my brother". I believe if we'll stop looking at our brothers and sisters as problems, we'll see a great release of spiritual, mental and physical health amongst the people of God. Say it to yourself when you're unsure of your feelings towards a fellow believer, "He's not heavy, he's my brother".

'So what I want to say,' concluded Jim, 'is that the Lord's Supper provides a glorious opportunity to reaffirm this kind of fellowship.'

When he had finished, the Elders gave room for the people to mingle and talk to one another. The Spirit of God was much in evidence and a number of folk were reconciled to each other. Others received words of encouragement. Several sick ones were prayed for and testified to healing. When the bread and wine were passed around the sense of God's shalom filled the grateful, joyful hearts of the congregation and they gave thanks to the Lord who had given himself for this end.

The Pilgrim Watcher stood at the side busily making notes. He was smiling. 'This is more to my liking,' he murmured to himself. 'Enough of this and the world will change!'

CHAPTER SIX

Think Well, Feel Well

'Some doctors and researchers estimate that between 60% and 90% of all illnesses are self-induced because of wrong attitudes and emotional responses.'

The comment came from Mr Christian as the bus upon which the four men were travelling climbed Highgate Hill and passed the Whittington Hospital. They were journeying to Hampstead to spend a day out discussing the relationship between mental and physical health. As soon as they had boarded the bus the Courier had opened the debate by asking whether they thought there really was a connection between the two.

It had been partly in response to the latter's entreaties that Mr Aquarius had rejoined the party. He had finally been persuaded by his wife. She insisted that their views ought to be heard, especially as the future well-being of society was at stake; never mind what Mr Christian thought.

Then there was the Pilgrim Watcher. Who was he? An extra-terrestrial time traveller? A highly developed mystic of great psychic power allowing him to dematerialize at will? Surely not an angel! Or was he what people in times past mistakenly called an angel? Either way, Mr Aquarius needed to be present to find out.

Finally, there was Susan to consider. She had now moved

out of the commune and taken a flat in Sundridge Park.
Dawn felt angry and concerned over the relationship which
was developing with the Courier, whom she could see was
coming strongly under Mr Christian's influence. Her husband ought to do all he could to prevent that. Hence, with
renewed purpose, he determined to make his voice felt in
the group.

'Are you saying then that most people have no need to be
in hospital because it's all in the mind?' the Courier queried,
in response to Mr Christian's comment.

'No, not in the way you mean,' he replied. 'I'm not
minimizing the reality of the illnesses or suggesting that
most of the patients are hypochondriacs. But I am saying
that mental attitudes have a profound effect on our state of
health. I think we saw a little of that when we attended Dr
Evans' lecture on stress. Do you remember?'

The others nodded.

'I agree with you entirely,' said Mr Aquarius, adding as
an afterthought, 'for a change!'

Mr Christian smiled. 'I'm glad to hear it, Leo. Though
how long it'll last, I wouldn't like to say!'

They were soon interrupted as the bus stopped at the
Spaniards Inn, where they alighted. The day was fine and
they strolled amicably towards the adjoining woods. Mr
Christian stopped at the edge of the woodland before a
massively ancient tree. The others looked at him, puzzled.

'This is where I first consciously began my journey into
Christian wholeness,' he explained. 'I was twelve at the
time, with no Christian background. My brothers and I
used to come here to play. There was nothing special about
the particular day but I shall never forget standing here
before this tree.

'You see, God revealed himself to me in that moment. I
became suddenly aware of his existence and of his holy
power and glory. I tell you, it scared me, because he told
me that we were on anything but friendly terms. But he also
let me know that one day I would serve him. It was another

three years or so before I realized what that meant and responded to Christ.'

Mr Aquarius gazed quizzically at the tree, his head slightly on one side. 'Why do you call what happened to you a meeting with God? I say what you experienced was simply a child's sense of awe at the grandeur of nature and the ageless life force which an old tree conveys. You can call it religious experience if you like, but I think that's only your interpretation of it.'

Mr Christian grinned. 'I won't argue with you over it. All I can say is that for me it was a genuine revelation which began to change my whole outlook on life. I knew I'd met God, in the way that Paul describes when he says, "Ever since the creation of the world his invisible nature, namely, his eternal power and deity, has been clearly perceived in the things that have been made" (Romans 1:20). By the way, he goes on to speak of those who exchange the truth about God for a lie and worship and serve the creature rather than the Creator. I think that's what you're really doing, Leo, in the way you approach nature.'

'Here we go again,' sighed the Courier to the Pilgrim Watcher. 'Come on, you two. And what's this got to do with mental attitudes to health, anyway?'

'Quite a lot, you'll see,' Mr Christian shouted across to him. 'Our inner attitudes are determined by what we believe. Haven't you got hold of that yet?'

'It's coming. It's coming,' the other replied good-naturedly.

When they had settled down in a clearing, the Pilgrim Watcher, quill at the ready, asked them to explain how mental and emotional outlooks affected general health.

Sunlight streamed through the fresh spring-leaved trees. New fronds of bracken were slowly uncurling from their winter's bed and stretching their slender green arms towards the sun. The earthy smell of the air was clean and invigorating.

'This is what I mean really,' Mr Christian explained.

'On days like this we feel healthy. These beautiful surroundings make us think positively and lay aside our cares for a while. That has an immediate effect on our overall health. If somebody joined us now with a streaming cold we'd far less likely catch it than if, say, it was a dismal grey day and we were thoroughly depressed with everything about us.'

'Certainly,' agreed the Courier. 'But we can hardly control the weather, can we now? Especially in this country!'

'No, all I'm saying is, be in a good mood and your resistance to disease will go up. We may feel especially cheerful today because of our pleasant environment but I believe, as a Christian, that it's possible to be positive even in depressing situations.'

'Yes, we don't always have control over our surroundings,' agreed Mr Aquarius. 'But we can control our response to them. But before we talk about that I would like to point out that positive attitudes produce much more than just resistance to viruses. In fact, as you know, I think the whole approach of orthodox medicine is suspect at this point. Conventional doctors far too easily blame bacteria and viruses for complaints, whereas I believe it's much more to do with imbalances in a person's total ecosystem.'

He proceeded to say that negative responses not only leave us vulnerable to short term sicknesses but, by upsetting the body's chemical and immune systems, they themselves produce chronic complaints such as arthritis, hypertension, spastic colon, cancer and goodness knows what else.

The present age is rife with disease because people have either failed to recognize this or, more likely, have done nothing about it. In fact, the connection between tension and ulcers has been known for a long time, but people have not been taught by the medical profession, or anyone else for that matter, the secrets of stress-free living.

To illustrate his point, Mr Aquarius invited them to flex their biceps and hold the position as long as possible, an act which was a decidedly odd spectacle to the middle-aged woman out walking her dog.

She stopped, stared, then hurried rapidly away in the direction from which she had come.

'I hope this isn't one of your meditation exercises, Leo,' laughed Mr Christian. 'My arms are beginning to ache.'

'Well, that's enough,' he replied. 'You can stop now because it's made my point. You see, after a while our arms hurt because the muscles were under tension. If that had been sustained we would eventually have damaged them. Now what I'm trying to get across is that negative attitudes tense up muscles all over our bodies even though we may be completely unaware of it. Then slowly, insidiously, the damage is done. General muscular tension alone will raise our blood pressure and put our hearts under extra strain. A constantly knotted-up abdomen will probably produce a stomach ulcer sooner or later.'

'And there are destructive emotions which produce excess fatty acids in the blood and joints, leading to slow degeneration of the tissues,' chipped in Mr Christian.

'That's right,' Mr Aquarius agreed. 'Now, my concern is that a lot of research has been done into this but most people still don't know how to detect when things are going wrong or know what to do about it. What we need is a way of monitoring our moods. Fortunately, there's a technique available for that purpose today. It's called biofeedback.'

'That's not the same as biorhythms, is it?' asked the Pilgrim Watcher, bemused by these strange terms.

'No, but they're related. Your biorhythms will tell you what times to be specially on guard. Biofeedback enables you to monitor and control your reactions to life at all times.'

Autogenics means literally "self-originating" and refers to the ability of the mind to regulate its own and the body's processes, especially those over which normally we have no control, the involuntary ones such as heartbeat and brain activity. This is the principle underlying biofeedback. The technique normally consists of relaxation training practised in conjunction with the use of instruments which measure, for example, blood pressure, pulse rate, skin resistance and brain wave patterns.

This feedback of information concerning the biological functions indicates a person's current state of relaxation. He then concentrates on being aware of how he is feeling and seeks to improve the readings by the exercise of "mind over matter". Although essentially a preventive treatment, claims are made for its effectiveness in controlling palpitations, epilepsy and migraine, amongst other conditions.

'It really fulfills the old proverb, "As a man thinketh, so is he," Mr Aquarius enthused. 'If everybody learned how to do this, we'd solve most of the mood-induced diseases. There are portable machines available now for taking readings but after a while you don't even need one of those. You become aware of the feelings and exercise control almost automatically. Now you don't think that's demonic, do you?' he challenged Mr Christian.

'I think it comes under your general heading of spirits of legalism and humanism, doesn't it?' suggested the Courier, before the other could reply. 'But it seems to make good sense to me. What have you, I mean *we*, Christians got to offer as an alternative if we don't like this approach?'

Mr Christian chewed on a blade of grass for a few moments before replying. Then he opened his Bible at the book of Proverbs.

'Let me read you a couple of verses,' he said. 'Here's the first, which you've heard before, Dai, Proverbs 14:30, "A tranquil mind gives life to the flesh, but passion makes the bones rot." The other is in chapter 17:22, "A cheerful heart is a good medicine, but a downcast spirit dries up the bones."

'God made us of interrelated parts—spirit, soul and body. These are not separate entities having nothing to do with one another but each aspect of our nature affects the others,' he explained. 'Theologians are missing the whole

point when they argue about whether we're two-part or
three-part creatures. Actually, we're one-part! At best we
can only very loosely define different aspects of our being.
For example, people are debating at the moment whether
the mind is simply to be equated with the brain or whether
it's more than that. If the former, then mind is part of the
body. If the latter, is mind the same as spirit? Or is mind the
soul? Actually, I believe mind is both physical and non-
physical. Is that a definition of a soul?'

'Hang on! Hang on!' cried the Courier. 'This is going to
get very confusing.'

'That's the whole point,' Mr Christian replied. 'You
can't make neat little definitions about human nature.
That's what the behaviourists tried to do. But it's hardly a
credible position nowadays when we're gaining increasing
evidence of the non-material parts of nature. I believe, of
course, that man does have a spiritual dimension to his
being. And, along with the Scriptures, I consider that to be
the most important part, and it has a great influence upon
our outer nature.'

'So you do agree with me that maintaining a right outlook
is the main key to living in health and wholeness?' Mr
Aquarius asked.

'I'd go further and say that a positive inner life *is* health
and wholeness. Once that's right and we've learned how to
maintain it, substantial bodily health follows more or less
automatically. At least, that's what I understand Proverbs
to be saying.'

'This is all very well,' the Courier persisted. 'You two
seem fairly agreed. But how *as a Christian* do you maintain
this kind of positive life?'

Mr Christian replied that this was where he and Mr
Aquarius were bound to part company. Secular man sees
negative emotions as psychological problems in need of
adjustment. The only debate really is over how that should
be done, by drug therapy, electric shock or group therapy
on the one hand or by self-help methods such as yoga,

meditation and biofeedback on the other.

The Christian, however, views negative emotions in general as sin. It is sinful to be angry, jealous, argumentative, anxious, selfish and lustful. And because these things are sins they bring their own judgement upon those who live like that. This may come quickly or be a cumulative process over the years. Psalm 107:17 says, 'Some were sick through their sinful ways, and because of their iniquities suffered affliction.' The solution to their need was to cry to the Lord their deliverer. Verse 20 declares, 'He sent forth his word, and healed them.' The prime answer to negativeness is the gospel.

'But you're not saying that Christians never get depressed or screwed up with life, are you?' asked Mr Aquarius incredulously.

'Not at all,' Mr Christian replied. 'In actual fact, the temptations which come upon believers are often greater than those experienced by unbelievers. We not only have all the usual trials of life but those which arise from persecution, from satanic attack and from the demanding work of serving the Lord. The apostle Paul himself went through one patch so bad that he said, "We were so utterly, unbearably crushed that we despaired of life itself" (2 Corinthians 1:8). That's honest confession for you! Mind, he came through triumphant, nonetheless.'

'Tell us what the secret is,' said the Pilgrim Watcher.

'It's an inbuilt mood-monitor,' Mr Christian responded brightly. 'No, it's not an implanted biofeedback machine but the Holy Spirit himself. When he takes up residence in our bodies he begins to change our temperaments so that we become like Jesus. We're like gardens which have been neglected, full of weeds and diseases. The Spirit clears these away and plants good things. Let me quote you the kind of fruit which he produces. It's in Galatians 5:22–23. "But the fruit of the Spirit is love, joy, peace, patience, kindness, goodness, faithfulness, gentleness, self-control." Any believer, whatever his temperament or background, can live with that kind of outlook if he permits the Holy Spirit to work in his life. And that kind of person will tend to be healthy in body too.'

He explained that it takes a bit of time for some believers to get into this, particularly those who are negative thinkers. The depressives, the restless, the aggressive all need special grace from God and a willingness to be taught by the Spirit. It really is quite unnecessary for a Christian to excuse his negative behaviour or thought patterns by saying, 'That's just the way I'm made.' God is in the remaking business and the Holy Spirit transforms temperaments! We need only to yield ourselves into his hands day by day and let him do it.

'Not surprisingly, the incidence of disease is significantly lower amongst those who walk by the Spirit,' Mr Christian continued. 'It's just a fulfilment of those two proverbs I read earlier. It's also true that Spirit-filled people are likely to make speedier recoveries from illness when it does occur.'

'You make it sound so easy,' protested Mr Aquarius. 'You're claiming that what mystics and holy men and people like myself spend years seeking can be anyone's, just like that! You have no techniques, no equipment. It simply happens by letting it!'

'Well, it's simple really,' Mr Christian replied quietly. 'You seek oneness with the Force, Leo, but I believe that's really serving Satan. He's a cruel master and will keep you chasing the wind to find the elusive balance and control you seek. He'll demand that the path be hard because you have to *earn* your reward. That's the nature of legalism.

'The God we serve is a God of love and grace. He makes no vain promises or excessive demands. He comes to our aid to do us good. All it requires is a humble heart to receive that grace every day—and health is ours!'

Mr Aquarius stood up. He spoke rather stiffly. 'Well, there we have it again. I'm of the devil, you're the ones who've got it right. If you don't mind, we'll leave it there for the moment. I'd like to take a stroll. I'll see you later, perhaps, at the pond. To be honest, I thought we were on our way to some agreement today, but it doesn't seem the case does it?'

And with that he strode off through the trees.

The Courier fiddled with a piece of grass. 'I think you've offended him again, Peter. Still, I hope he comes back. I expect he will, anyway.' He laughed. 'Hey, I'm hungry. How about a bite to eat at the Inn?'

The other two heartily agreed and together they set off to get some lunch.

*   *   *

After lunch they strolled towards Whitestone Pond and the airy slopes of Hampstead Heath, known as the Vale of Health, by Jack Straw's Castle.

'I've got a question for you about myself.' The Courier spoke to Mr Christian. 'I know that now the Lord is really in my life things will be different but I'm worried about one thing. It's just whether I'm going to get depressed again. You see, I'm so useless when that happens and I withdraw into myself. And there's Susan, see. I like her very much and, well, I don't want to make a mess of it. Do you understand what I mean?'

They walked on together in silence for a while as Mr Christian pondered how to reply. At length he spoke: 'The root of all depression is self-pity. I know that sounds a strong statement but I've found it to be generally true. Self-pity occurs when we've not found any satisfactory way of resolving our problems. For example, if my wife and I have an argument and don't settle it, I may feel a combination of regret and resentment. If I don't deal with that properly, say, by going and apologizing for my part in it, I'll begin to feel sorry for myself. It's only a short step from that to depression.'

The Courier nodded. 'I can see that. I suppose I was a permanent depressive because I had great unresolved root problems all through my life?'

'That's right. Rejection and hurt, especially, affect us in that sort of way. Anyhow, you've been freed from all that now and you've received the Holy Spirit!' Mr Christian replied cheerfully. 'Provided you keep in good fellowship with him, you'll live joyfully and confidently in the future.'

'How do you mean?'

'Well, I've remembered a statement by a Christian author, Tim La Haye. In one of his books he wrote, "Before a Spirit-filled believer can become depressed, he must grieve the Spirit through anger or quench the Spirit through fear."[1] In other words, those two reactions restrict the positive work of the Holy Spirit in our lives. Here, have you got a piece of paper and a pencil so I can illustrate how this happens?'

The Courier rummaged through his pockets and came up with an old envelope and a ball-point. Mr Christian stopped for a moment to draw a diagram. The Pilgrim Watcher peered over his shoulder with interest.

'Anger,' he said, includes related feelings of hatred, enmity, resentment, argumentativeness and bitterness, whether these are expressed against people, political systems or society in general. Either way, their effect is destructive, sometimes causing actual physical violence or accidents, or producing poisonous chemicals in the body which slowly erode health.

'From our Christian point of view, all this anger is sin and breaks our good fellowship with God. We grieve him— and if we don't do something about it we'll become sorry for ourselves and well on the road to depression.

[1] Tim LaHaye, *Spirit-controlled Temperament* (Kingsway Publications 1972) page 124.

'The same is true of fear. Again, we include related emotions such as anxiety, worry, timidity, shyness and so on. Fear paralyses us and renders us ineffective in our service for the Lord. It's the great crippling disease of the saints; hence, the constant scriptural encouragements to be strong and of good courage.'

Fear is very destructive; for example, it stimulates an excess of adrenalin which harms the body. Permanent anxiety produces rheumatoid arthritis. Fear of pregnancy can cause frigidity or miscarriage. Jesus said that in the last days men's hearts would fail them for fear. That may have a physical as well as psychological aspect to it. It is also an expression of unbelief and so hinders our walk with God.

'The antidote,' Mr Christian went on to say, 'is to deal with these feelings as soon as possible. Now, the way to dissipate anger is to express forgiveness. The moment we do that we're in the place where we can receive the Lord's forgiveness—and fellowship is restored. You remember the Lord's Prayer, "Forgive us our trespasses as we forgive those who trespass against us"?

'With fear, I believe that the best antidote is to declare the truth of God's word. You can do that in all sorts of ways. Perhaps a good Christian song will come to mind or some scripture you've memorized. Or just speaking out the truth. The word of faith will destroy fear.'

Mr Christian wrote some more on the back of the envelope so that it read like this:

ANGER

Forgiveness → BROKEN FELLOWSHIP → SELF PITY → DEPRESSION

FEAR
Word of faith   Re-filled with   God's comfort   Joy and
                       the Spirit   worship

The Courier looked at it for a few moments before commenting. When he did, he raised a difficulty he had with 'the word of faith'.

'I can see that all you're saying makes excellent sense, but isn't there a danger that the word of faith will be just saying positive things without any reality behind it? Like the insecure woman standing in front of the mirror repeating over and over again, "You are beautiful. People do like you. You are not inadequate." Or that song from *The King and I*, "Whenever I feel afraid I whistle a happy tune". Do you know what I mean?'

The Pilgrim Watcher, who had walked behind them in silence until now, broke into the conversation.

'One of the observations I have made of this generation of men is that they are obsessed with things that are negative,' he said. 'You are very good at exposing evil but do not know how to exalt goodness. I see people entertaining themselves on a diet of violence, suffering and death. I perceive critical documentary films which show the faults of men but say little about their virtues. It is a cynical age and full of disbelief.'

'You're beginning to sound like me,' laughed the Courier, to which the Pilgrim Watcher protested that he was only doing his job.

'What you are really saying is that the climate in which we live doesn't encourage faith. We tend to see the dark side of things,' said Mr Christian.

'Yes, and it is even more apparent to me, for I see the powers of evil but I see even more clearly the glory of the Most High and the triumph of the Lamb. I wish you believers would not stare so wide-eyed at the Enemy but would let your hearts be thrilled at the might of your Lord. Have you not read the Scriptures, "And the light shineth in the darkness; and the darkness comprehended it not"? And nor shall it ever.' The Pilgrim Watcher spoke with absolute assurance. He continued: 'You must open your eyes to the truth of things as they are in reality. Your Lord and mine is reigning over all things and nothing is outside the compass of his control. *That* is the truth!'

The two men were silent for a few moments as they let his

words sink in.

'Do you know the old couplet which goes like this?' said Mr Christian to the Courier. '"Two men looked through the same prison bars; one saw mud, and the other saw stars." The mud and the stars are both true but the degree of hope you experience is determined by which one you concentrate upon.'

'Yes,' he agreed. 'We do seem to be bogged down in the mud these days. And the street lights have more or less blotted out the stars, haven't they?'

'That's actually a good way of putting it. True faith has to contend both with "the mud" and "the street lights" in order to experience spiritual reality. But reality it is, for all that,' Mr Christian replied. 'It's no folly to make good faith-confessions based on truth.

'My wife and I had an experience like this recently. We woke up and found it was one of those really disgusting days. Pouring with rain, cold, bleak and grey. We felt ratty from the start and everybody seemed to be getting on one another's nerves. I said, "This is a spiritually dangerous day for us. We'll really make a mess of things if we're not careful." She agreed and we began to make good confessions about the Lord, about each other and even about the day. You know, "This is the day the Lord has made; we will rejoice and be glad in it", and so on.

'It didn't stop the rain but our attitudes changed, with the result that we both had a super day and were able to cheer a lot of other people up as well. Somehow, our faith-confessions took our spirits behind the scenes so that we were aware of God's love and purpose for that day and were able to rejoice.'

'So are you saying that Christians should be happy all the time?' the Courier asked.

'What I'm saying is that God invites us in every situation to enter into his joy. "The joy of the Lord is your strength" (Nehemiah 8:10). James says we're to count it all joy when we meet various trials, because we can see the Lord's good purposes behind them. That's not the same as a happy-go-lucky attitude which refuses to take life seriously. We face very grave issues at times but always with God's presence and peace.'

By now they had reached the pond. They stood looking out over the Vale of Health, exhilarated by the luminous sense of light and space which it conveyed.

'Gosh, this does you good just to look at it, eh?' exclaimed the Courier.

'Truly the Lord has made all things well,' replied the Pilgrim Watcher.

When they were sitting down, the Courier addressed Mr Christian.

'So, let me see if I've got this right. What you've been saying is that the Holy Spirit himself is really the source of positive thinking and, therefore, of health within us. Provided we don't grieve him or quench him we're able to live in the Lord's joy. And that includes making positive confessions of the Lord's truth, never mind what our circumstances are like. Is that right?'

Mr Christian agreed that it was so. Positive thinking based upon the truth of God is not self-deception at all but an expression of faith in God. People who live like that both please the Lord and reap the blessings of health and healing.

'There's a terrific piece of wisdom in Paul's letter to the Philippians,' he continued. 'It says, "Rejoice in the Lord always; again I will say, rejoice. Let all men know your forbearance. The Lord is at hand. Have no anxiety about anything, but in everything by prayer and supplication with thanksgiving let your requests be made known to God. And the peace of God, which passes all understanding, will keep your hearts and your minds in Christ Jesus" (Philippians 4:4–7).

'The more we learn to praise God and delight in his ways, the more we know of his peace. If only we'll give thanks without fear we shall be kept in wholeness.'

'You know,' said the Courier, 'When I first came to one

of your meetings I felt what it was like to really rejoice. I was so uplifted, I can't describe it. Until then I'd always thought of worship as a heavy-going affair.'

To which the Pilgrim Watcher laughed. 'You wait until you are before the Lord face to face. Assuredly, heaven is not sombre!'

'When God's people gather it should be an expression of deep joy in God,' affirmed Mr Christian. 'And, if you remember, I said earlier that a cheerful heart is a good medicine—which means our praise meetings are also places of healing.'

'Do you mean you lay hands on the sick?' asked the Courier.

'We may do that,' he replied. 'But I mean something far more. I'll give you a couple of illustrations.

'Chloe was a lovely girl but a few years ago she was marred by a disfiguring skin complaint which affected her right arm so that the upper part was discoloured and spoiled. It seemed to be a permanent condition which she would just have to put up with. Well, she came along to one of our celebration meetings and gave herself to rejoicing in the Lord. It was one of those hot summer days so she wore a short-sleeved dress, in spite of her rash. Anyway, her friends at church never minded it. As the praise mounted she raised her hands to the Lord. Her heart was full of joy and thanksgiving to God for all his blessings. Whilst in this state she happened to open her eyes and glance at her arm. I guess the Lord directed her to do so. The skin was completely healed! Not a trace of discolouration remained.

'Or there's Alison, a young woman slowly crippling up with multiple sclerosis. She could scarcely walk when she came to the meeting and needed help from friends to hobble to her seat. But she loved the Lord and gave herself to praise. At the end of the meeting she needed to visit the toilet and made her way painfully and slowly to the steps leading out the back. To her utter amazement she suddenly found she could climb them without difficulty. She *ran* across the hall and, when her friends found her minutes later, she was jumping for joy and completely healed of her disease.

'That's what I mean,' Mr Christian enthused. 'Places of rejoicing are places of healing. Those who delight in God open themselves to the Lord's wholeness. I'm sure there are countless stories of this kind of thing.'

Just then they were interrupted by a shout. It was Mr Aquarius, looking a lot happier. He came across to them accompanied by a loudly-dressed woman. He introduced her as Wilma Bakewell. Her mid-West drawl quickly betrayed her American origins.

'Wilma is an old friend of ours,' he explained. 'I didn't know she was in this country so nobody was more surprised than I when we bumped into each other just now.'

'Well, hi there,' she enthused in response, beaming all over her face. 'Hey, this is a fine little ol' view you've got here. Not quite Gran' Canyon, but not bad!'

The Pilgrim Watcher judged that he was going to be very invisible to Wilma Bakewell.

'Dawn and I first met Wilma in the early sixties,' Mr Aquarius continued. 'We were all students in London at the time.'

'Gee, honey, don't remind me! You make me feel kinda old all of a sudden,' she gently scolded him.

'So are you over here on holiday?' Mr Christian enquired politely.

'Yeah, sort of. Actually,' she confided in a none too quiet voice, 'I'm getting over a divorce.'

'Oh, I'm sorry to hear that.'

'Well, don't be. He was a no good jerk, in any case. No better than the one before either. Still, I've done all right out of it, so I guess I'll be okay.'

Mr Christian sighed inwardly. Divorce itself was awful enough but why were some people so brazen about it? The Courier must have been having the same thought because he suddenly blurted out, 'How on earth can you be so matter of fact about it?'

Before she could reply, Mr Aquarius cut in. 'I'm sure Wilma doesn't mean to sound quite like that, Dai. Mind you,' he added, with a smile towards her, 'you always were a hard-headed pragmatist, weren't you?'

'You mean, I hire 'em and fire 'em, just like a business?' she laughed. 'Well, I suppose I am what y'd call a successful business woman. But no,' she became serious for a moment, 'truth is, you guys, it hurts like hell. This is jest ma way of handlin' it.'

Mr Aquarius broke the moment of awkward silence.

'Still, if you don't mind I'm going to take Wilma back to see Dawn,' he said. 'No doubt I'll see you again quite soon. Be in touch.'

'So long,' said Wilma. 'Nice meeting y'all.'

'Phew!' breathed the Courier when they had gone. 'Not Leo's normal type, I'd say.'

'No,' replied Mr Christian, smiling. 'But interesting the reference to pragmatism and business. It ties in with what we were saying earlier about positive thinking. I'm over-simplifying it, but if truth is what works then the pursuit of success is a noble end.'

'You're not suggesting that we should be like that are you?' exclaimed the Courier.

'No, not at all', laughed Mr Christian in reply. 'Though you'll find this philosophy influencing parts of the church today through what is popularly called "health and wealth theology" or "prosperity teaching". You'll doubtless come across it sooner or later, so it's best to be warned.'

'Tell me about it.'

Mr Christian explained briefly that there are some Christians, particularly in the U.S.A. and South Africa, who, consciously or unconsciously, interpret the Scriptures on the basis of this success-orientated philosophy and come up with something which is essentially a christianized version of the secular 'power of positive thinking' technique. Proponents of this doctrine often make unqualified statements such as, 'God wants you to be wealthy'; 'No Christian should ever be poor'; 'Perfect health is your birthright'; 'If you die before seventy, you've allowed the devil to snatch you away'. Lack of faith is attributed to those who fail to live like this.

' "Prosperity teaching" is suspect for a number of reasons, not least for its selective use of scripture. It picks only the positive texts and neglects those which teach that 'through many tribulations we must enter the kingdom of God', (Acts 14:22). It puts a tremendous pressure on the poor and sick to 'believe' which often results only in self-condemnation. It divides Christians very quickly into the haves and have-nots on the basis of external success rather than godly hearts, an emphasis which belongs to the Old Covenant rather than the New. There is more than a suspicion, too, of pagan, class-ridden materialism behind it all, which one would expect from a pragmatic root-philosophy. In short, it is over-simplistic teaching which is both biblically and pastorally unsound.'

'You want me to keep right away from all that?' nodded the Courier.

Mr Christian laughed. 'This may surprise you, but I would say actually we need to hear something from these people.'

The Courier looked puzzled, so he explained: 'There is across Great Britain what I can only describe as a 'poverty spirit'. It is the spirit of mediocrity, low expectation and compromise. It springs out of the general cynicism of our times. Unfortunately, Christians seem especially affected by it; the church is full of unbelief. This is why we see so little healing and why so many projects suffer for lack of adequate finance. We simply do not expect it. And when we do turn to the positive promises of the Scriptures, we are apt to do them to death by a thousand qualifications.

'I believe God is allowing this extreme and polluted stream of teaching to hit the church over here for the sole purpose of jerking us awake,' he declared. 'It's a sledgehammer to crack a tough nut, if you like. So, though I can't accept that it's biblically sound, and it raises many pastoral problems, nonetheless I welcome the prophetic nature of its positive thrust.'

'So be it!' exclaimed the Pilgrim Watcher.

'Well, I can see it's much better to expect to live in health and wealth than to have faith for being sick and poor!' the Courier responded dryly.

'Yes,' replied Mr Christian. 'I believe the time has come for God's people in this country to shake off their poverty, not out of selfishness, but in order to establish the kingdom of God in unshakable glory across the land. Think positively, because your God reigns!'

The afternoon sun was creating a shimmering haze which dazzled the eyes. The Pilgrim Watcher stood up and announced his temporary departure. An ethereal brilliance surrounded his tall form until he fragmented into a kaleidoscope of colours and was gone.

'I wish I knew how he does that!' said Mr Christian.

'One day. One day,' replied the Courier.

CHAPTER SEVEN

Work, Rest and Play

The Courier gasped for breath, his heart felt fit to explode within his breast, sweat poured from his body, salty tears stung his eyes, his legs were like jelly.

Along the river bank, through the park, up a killingly steep hill, the high path, then dropping away, climbing the winding woodland trail—and then all the way back. He couldn't remember the last time he had run so far. What a fool to have come! How much further? Ah, thank goodness for that; the end in sight.

Mr Christian stood waiting, himself breathless but laughing as the Courier staggered to the end and collapsed on the ground.

'Not bad, Dai, considering it's your first run in years. A few more weeks and you'll be fit as a fiddle.'

'You've got to be joking,' the Courier panted. 'I tell you, boyo, I was thinking some pretty evil thoughts back there!'

It was seven-thirty in the morning and the sun was already warm. Mr Christian ran most mornings and the Courier, to his regret, had volunteered to give it a try. He had been a good runner at school, after all. Now they sat on a bench whilst he gasped for breath and accepted that years of inactivity had taken their toll. Eventually he found wind enough to speak.

'You don't expect all Christians to do this every day, do you?'

His friend laughed, 'No, of course not. This just happens to be my particular way of keeping fit.'

'You think it's important to do that, though?'

'Yes, I do, actually. I know a lot of Christians don't agree with me, or at least, agree only in theory, but more and more of us are seeing this as part of a responsible stewardship of the bodies the Lord has given us.

'It's all right if you have a job which involves heavy physical labour, but the trend in our society is away from that and now we have large numbers of people who live pretty sedentary lives,' he explained. 'Even housework is much easier than ever before—though my wife seldom agrees with me on that! Many factories are largely automated and manual work may well become virtually a thing of the past. In addition, cars and public transport have made walking all but redundant for most of us. That's why we're such an unfit generation.'

Lack of regular exercise gives rise to many problems. Physiologists are agreed that the human frame was designed for hard work and, within reasonable limits, keeps healthy that way. When we don't exercise the metabolism becomes sluggish and this allows the build up of toxins and deposits in the body. Cancer cells, for example, are being randomly produced all the time but a fit person tends to destroy them quickly. In the unfit there is a greater likelihood that such cells will proliferate. Though this is not the only cause of cancer; which is why well-known sporting personalities may still be afflicted with the disease.

Recent years have focused on the debate about the effects of saturated fats in producing high levels of cholesterol in the blood which then gets laid down as deposits in the arteries. A whole new industry of polyunsaturated margarine production has sprung up as a result. However, this theory is now being challenged and attention is moving back to levels of fitness rather than diet as the main cause of the problem. Hard physical exercise causes blood vessels to dilate and toxins to be expelled from the body. It's a bit like giving a car a good long drive. The overall improvement in circulation is also good for the brain as well as for the bodily extremities.

'I'm told that marathon runners are immune to heart disease,' Mr Christian continued. 'Certainly aerobic or cardio-vascular exercise greatly strengthens the heart muscle and reduces both the rate at which it needs to pump and the resistance which it encounters. As you know, heart disease is a major killer in this country.'

He said that although exercise by itself won't lead to substantial weight loss, it does increase the rate at which we consume energy and makes it harder for fat to be laid down. It creates energy reserves and also strengthens our resistance to disease. Adrenalin and noradrenalin are released in a healthy manner; which helps fight depression. Depressives generally have low levels of these hormones.

'That's all very well,' said the Courier, who was feeling better by now. 'But this is only good secular commonsense. Can't a Christian just believe God for all these benefits without going through the agony I endured this morning?'

'Well, the pain only lasts for a short while when you first start exercising. But, really, it's to do with how you understand wholeness,' his companion replied. 'You see, as I've said before, Christianity really is the most physical of all the great world religions. Whereas most of them either indulge the body at will because it's unimportant, or, more likely, seek to subdue it because they believe it to be inherently evil, we honour our bodies as no less than the Lord's houses. Paul said, "Do you not know that your body is a temple of the Holy Spirit within you?" (1 Corinthians 6:19). True holiness isn't just a matter of being "spiritual" but of presenting our bodies to God as instruments of righteousness. That's what Paul says in Romans 6:13. So true spirituality is concerned about the use of our bodies.

'The greatest evidence for the nobility of human flesh is

found in Jesus himself. When God desired to send his Son into the world, he didn't send a spirit but a body. Hebrews 10:5 declares of Jesus, "...a body hast thou prepared for me." The miracle of the incarnation is that the eternal Son took real, ordinary human flesh and showed us how it was meant to be used when filled with the Holy Spirit. The superspiritual and today's mystics like to play this down, just as they did in New Testament times.

'But John will have none of it. He writes in 1 John 4:2–3: "Every spirit which confesses that Jesus Christ has come in the flesh is of God, and every spirit which does not confess Jesus is not of God." A real man was born, lived, learned, ate, drank, did good, died on a cross and was physically raised from the dead.'

'So where does physical exercise come into it?' the Courier persisted.

'Well, in two ways, I believe,' Mr Christian replied. 'When God made Adam he gave him a physical occupation —to till the Garden of Eden. That's quite hard work, even without weeds! When Jesus came, of all the occupations he might have had, he chose the tough one of being a lumberjack and carpenter. Paul himself, like all good Pharisees, believed in the importance of manual work and so continued his trade as a tentmaker. And in any case, the whole lifestyle of those days was physically demanding. Those people were tough! I think we, with our soft way of life, need to take some steps in their direction.

'The other reason is this business of being a temple of the Holy Spirit. I believe I'm meant to be a good steward of my body and do my best to look after it. You see, we believers mustn't simply get into the world's current health kick. That's mostly motivated by secular considerations and self-centred desires to feel good and look better. Our bodies, however, exist to serve the Lord. That's our main reason for caring about them.

'Paul has something to say to Timothy on the subject. He says, "Train yourself in godliness; for while bodily training is of some value, godliness is of value in every way, as it holds promise for the present life and also for the life to come" (1 Timothy 4:7–8). Clearly, the priority of our lives must be to attain spiritual fitness. That brings blessing for both this life and the future. Physical fitness has very definite limitations; at best it can only bless us in the present. However, that doesn't mean it's without value.

'The way I see it is that I should make physical exercise an expression of my desires for godliness,' Mr Christian concluded. 'It's of value in helping my body serve the Lord. After all, an undisciplined body is harder to control when temptation comes. I guess this is what Paul meant when he said, "Every athlete exercises self-control in all things.... Well, I do not run aimlessly... but I pommel my body and subdue it."' (1 Corinthians 9:25–27.)

Just then, who should come running along the path but Susan. They were both surprised to see her out jogging and said as much.

'Hallo,' she puffed. 'I thought I might see you, Peter, 'cos I know you run this route, but Dai... I didn't expect you'd be out running!'

Mr Christian smiled as he watched Dai rise from his seat. That stomach hadn't been pulled in as far half an hour ago!

'Oh, yes,' he replied airily. 'I thought it was time I did some exercise. New lease of life and all that, you know. But I didn't know you were a runner, now.'

'Well, I only jog really. But I've been into this fitness thing ever since my back was better. Dawn recommended it. Now that's something I've been meaning to ask you, Peter. I've been attending an aerobics class. Is it all right for Christians to do that? I mean, it's not like yoga is it?'

'No, it's not at all like yoga,' Mr Christian replied. 'In fact, aerobics is quite a good means of exercise.'

'Not if you're a fellow, it isn't,' the Courier chipped in. 'I tried it once and it nearly crippled me for life!'

'That's 'cos you haven't got a woman's pelvis,' Susan laughed.

'Good thing too,' he retorted.

She explained that many of the exercises are only really suitable for a woman's frame but anyway, probably the Courier hadn't been to a proper class with a skilled instructor—and that was asking for trouble.

When Mr Christian asked her if she felt that there were any dangers in aerobics she replied that the biggest one is the temptation to set out to prove something. Some women are very much into the feminist thing and do aerobics because they want to be fitter and stronger than men. Others just get obsessed with their performance and push themselves too far. Susan felt if you don't enjoy your sport it isn't worth doing anyway. A sentiment to which Mr Christian heartily agreed.

'Well, I'm certainly not going to take up aerobics. So what should I do if I want to get fit? What kind of exercise is best for me?' asked the Courier.

'There are three things which you need a sport to do for you,' Susan answered. 'It should stretch your muscles so as to improve your flexibility. Then it should demand enough from you to strengthen your body. And, perhaps most important of all nowadays, it should really exercise your heart and lungs. That means to do any good it must raise your pulse rate above 130 beats per minute.'

'Yes, now what about this pulse thing?' Mr Christian asked. 'We hear a lot about people jogging and dropping dead with heart attacks and every book on the subject says don't exercise without taking medical advice. What do you reckon?'

'I think it's a matter of commonsense really,' she replied. 'Obviously if you haven't done any exercise for years it's no good charging straight into a game of squash or a marathon run.'

'You can say that again!' the Courier declared with feeling, giving Mr Christian a mock accusing glance.

'Well, you did want to come,' he retorted. 'But Susan's right. Unfit people or those above thirty-five do need to start gradually. Trevor Martin, in his book *Good Health!*, recommends a simple formula of two hundred minus your age, minus another forty if you're really unfit, as a starting limit for the pulse. You can reduce the handicap as you get fitter.'

'The other thing to do is to warm up first with a few stretches,' Susan added. 'That not only helps prevent damaged tendons but gets your heart rate going. If you shoot off from cold there's a real danger of it getting out of beat—and that's not good for you.'

'Okay. So I've got to be careful. But what should I do?' persisted the Courier.

'Find something you like and that meets your needs,' replied Mr Christian. 'I think in your case, Dai, it should be a sport which involves you with others.'

'Running, swimming and cycling are all good ways of exercising,' Susan said, 'And so are squash, badminton and tennis. Or there's football, rugby and cricket. Golf and bowls are fun but won't actually get you very fit. And there's always aerobics, of course!'

'Well, I'm not coming running with you, that's for sure,' the Courier said to Mr Christian with a laugh. 'At least, not until I'm a bit fitter.'

'Tell you what, why don't you go jogging with Susan in the mornings?' suggested Mr Christian.

They looked at each other and laughed.

'I think that's a good idea,' said Susan.

'Yes, we'll do that,' answered the Courier to Mr Christian with a grin, and blessed him in his heart.

'Right,' replied the latter. 'Well, I'm off for a shower. See you both later. We're meeting the others up town after lunch to talk about rest and meditation, Dai. Don't forget!'

*   *   *

It's the traffic mostly; the throbbing, drumming roar, the squeal of tyres, whining acceleration, impatient hooting. It makes the City of London an exceedingly noisy place. The wise look for the quiet places in which to spend their lunch breaks.

One such haven is the cool, light, little Norwegian Church of St Olave's tucked away in narrow Hart Street. It was here that the party gathered around two-thirty in the afternoon. Office workers who used the place at lunch times for prayer had returned to their businesses and the occasional tramps with their hard luck stories had moved on; so all was quiet and suitable for conversation. However, each sat in silence for a while, drinking in the peace of the building and admiring the simple architecture.

Mr Christian broke the stillness.

'All the troubles of life come upon us because we refuse to sit quietly for a while each day in our rooms. That's what Blaise Pascal wrote.'

'Ah, those were different days,' responded the Pilgrim Watcher. 'There was less noise and hurry. But I remember there was also much opposition when he came to know the Lord for himself. You recall that his book *Provincial Letters* was forbidden because he wrote therein of the need for divine grace!'

'Well, if he felt the need for quietness in those days, how much more do we need it in these,' commented the Courier.

'Yes, your world is not spoken of for its meditation,' replied the Pilgrim Watcher. 'I perceive that people do not have occupations which allow for contemplation. But neither do they meditate when they go home.'

'Ah, that's largely because of the television,' said Mr Christian. 'What one of my friends recently dubbed "the moron's magnet". It fixes the gaze but doesn't permit the mind to think. People sit there half absorbed, in almost total apathy. At the end of an evening they haven't learned anything of real value or allowed their own thoughts to develop. It's a kind of nightly state of suspended animation.'

'Which is why we need some sort of discipline to develop the art of meditation if people are to be whole,' Mr Aquarius came in. 'I know what you're going to say,' he added hastily. 'All meditation is of the devil.'

'No, I'm not,' retorted Mr Christian. 'I believe meditation is very important. It's just that your way is spiritually dangerous. As I said before, your search for detachment leaves you open to evil spirits. And not only that, it's legalistic.'

'Can you explain what you mean by that?' asked the Courier.

Mr Christian nodded and reached for a Bible in the pew rack. He turned to Matthew 11:28–30 and read aloud: ' "Come to me all who labour and are heavy laden, and I will give you rest. Take my yoke upon you, and learn from me; for I am gentle and lowly in heart, and you will find rest for your souls. For my yoke is easy, and my burden is light." '

'The way of God's wholeness is not one of hard discipline and arduous self-denial. You don't have to go through long rituals, elaborate exercises or special chants. All we really have to do is share in the life of Jesus. When we team up with him we find it an easy path to walk.

'Now there have always been those who've made the road to wholeness a hard one, even in the name of Christ,' he continued. 'People like the early Pillar Saints who sat on top of poles in order to be detached from the world, hermits, monks, mystics enduring long fasts and vigils; flagellants who scourged themselves. But these are not of the spirit of Christ.

'God's way is one of walking by faith and sharing Christ's peace. There's no technique for this because it's a total outlook on life.'

'Does this mean you have nothing else you can say?' questioned Mr Aquarius.

'Not at all. Sharing Jesus' yoke has some very practical implications,' Mr Christian replied. 'But let me tell you of my personal experience some years ago.

'Hebrews 4:9–11 says, "There remains a sabbath rest for the people of God; for whoever enters God's rest also ceases

from his labours as God did from his. Let us therefore strive
to enter that rest." When I was about seventeen years old I
went through a very bad patch. Partly, it was the identity
crisis which most young people experience at that age but I
was also wrestling with the will of God concerning a girl.
On top of this I coveted a motorcycle but couldn't raise the
money to buy one. All in all I was hit by a bout of depression.

'So one day, there I was standing on a London Underground platform frustrated, miserable and uptight. I looked
at the rails and contemplated suicide. Life was so unjust.
"What's the point of going on?" I thought. "I can't cope
with all these pressures any more."

'I didn't jump. The train came in and I got on. I glanced
at my watch. If the train didn't get a move on I knew I'd be
late for my appointment. It didn't! Slowly it chugged into
the interchange. I rushed from the doors, frantically
searching for the directions; along the platform, a race
down a tunnel, left turn, right turn, another tunnel, a flight
of steps, the platform. Which one? Right or left? The left
one. The train was in. The doors were closing. I leapt
through the diminishing gap, tussled with the doors, and
collapsed, exhausted and sweating, into the nearest seat.
Then God spoke.

'I opened my eyes and straight before me amongst the
row of advertisements was a text from Isaiah 26:3: "Thou
wilt keep him in perfect peace, whose mind is stayed on
thee, because he trusteth in thee."

'That's when I first began to learn the secret of living in
wholeness,' he said. 'I needed to learn how to fix my mind
on the Lord and let him do the worrying for me. I had to
trust him and let go of all my strivings and desires.

'So many people live frenetic lives, worrying, fretting,
planning for the future. Remember Dr Evans' lecture? God
doesn't want his people living like that. You know, one of
my favourite verses is in Psalm 127: "Unless the Lord builds
the house, those who build it labour in vain...it is in vain
that you rise up early and go late to rest, eating the bread of

anxious toil; for he gives to his beloved sleep."

'People are running themselves into the ground these days for all sorts of futile causes. And Christians themselves can so easily get caught up in this rat-race. I firmly believe the Lord wants us to move in peace and security so that we rule our circumstances instead of letting them overtake us. *That's* supernatural living.'

'And you believe that comes about by fixing our minds on the Lord?' asked the Courier.

Mr Christian nodded.

'But that's something we've to learn,' the Courier said. 'I guess many Christians aren't doing this automatically.'

'Yes, we have to learn how to meditate properly so that it becomes a way of life.'

'Hah!' cried Mr Aquarius. 'So you *do* have a technique. See, I knew it!'

Mr Christian tried to protest but the Pilgrim Watcher came to his aid.

'Whilst I have been here I have been observing how Christians conduct their devotions,' he said. 'And I must say, I am not happy with what I see.'

Mr Aquarius pressed him to explain.

'I observe sleepy saints who ease their consciences by reading a piece of scripture and reciting a list of requests,' he replied. 'Few seem either excited or much moved by the event. It is a ritual which means little to them.'

'Well, what do you have to say to that?' demanded Mr Aquarius. 'At least my meditation technique works. If he's right, yours doesn't.'

Mr Christian answered by dissociating himself from these so-called 'quiet times' which are fruitless religious exercises. He felt that it is, however, a good thing to set aside time to be alone with God. After all, Jesus said, "When you pray, go into your room and shut the door and pray to your Father" (Matthew 6:6).

'The important thing is to meet with God in a living way and to talk over the things of life with him. This doesn't require any particular time or place or posture; it can happen anywhere. But it helps to build it into our lifestyle somewhere. According to Isaiah's prophecy, Jesus would experience this each new day. "Morning by morning he wakens, he wakens my ear to hear as those who are taught" (Isaiah 50:4). There is no doubt that for many believers, like Jesus, the uncluttered early part of the day is a good time during which to meditate.'

'I'm beginning to do that,' said the Courier. 'What with jogging as well, my mornings are becoming quite busy! But I'm finding a problem with my thoughts wandering all over the place.'

'What you need is a mantra to chant,' said Mr Aquarius mischieviously. 'Seriously though, that's why we have one. We focus on the sound and that releases us from the limitations of our minds and into spiritual dimensions.'

'I'm sure Peter isn't going to agree with that, Leo. Are you, Peter?'

'No, of course not,' he replied shortly. 'But there's a couple of things you can do about wandering thoughts. The first is to take note of them because they are obviously things on your mind. Pray about them. Write them down. You know, sometimes we can't sleep or we wake up in the night because of a headful of thoughts. Don't fight it; it's usually a call to prayer. David spoke of meditating on God in the watches of the night. All these thoughts and ideas which buzz around need relating to him so that we see how God is at work in them.'

'What's the other thing?'

'Meditate with an open Bible,' Mr Christian suggested. 'The first Psalm says blessed is the man whose "Delight is in the law of the Lord, and on his law he meditates day and night" (Psalm 1:1–2). That's the great difference between us and other meditators. They seek to empty the mind in order to find truth in some abstract mystical experience; we fill our minds with living truth. Now that *can* degenerate into a mere ritual, but if you discuss what you are reading with the Lord, as you read, it will remain full of life and be a true spiritual experience. You'll know such intimate fellowship that, at times, you'll lose all sense of earth-boundness. But it'll be safe because it's in the Lord and his truth.

'Sometimes you'll be caught up in praise—then it won't be a "quiet time"!' He laughed. 'You'll speak in tongues as your spirit delights in God and your mind meditates on him. Now I don't know what that does for our alpha-waves or blood pressure, because nobody to my knowledge has measured the effects; but it has a mighty good influence on our well-being, that's for sure.'

'One other thing; you mentioned earlier a sabbath rest. What do you mean by that?' the Courier asked. 'See, I used to have Sundays in the valleys. That was the day when we weren't allowed hardly to breathe. We sat in boring chapel, went to boring Sunday School and read boring books at home in the meantime. It was a day of best clothes and best behaviour, and no fun.'

'Yes, I'll say this much for you Christians,' said Mr Aquarius. 'You certainly know how to put people off your faith! My Sundays weren't quite as bad as Dai's but I was still glad when they were over. I mean, do you still want to close all the shops and petrol stations and lock us all up in church for the day?'

Mr Christian was silent for a moment. What a tragedy that the faith which is so liberating, so exhilarating and glorious should ever be allowed to degenerate into yet another rule-bound religion. Jesus came to give life in its fullness and said the sabbath was designed as a servant for man's benefit; we were not made in order to serve the sabbath. That put him into immediate conflict with the religious leaders of the day, whose Spirit-less ethics could do no more than insist on outward conformity to rules as the mark of piety. God keep the church from pharisaism in the name of Christ!

'Those people had it all wrong,' he blurted out. 'And I'm

deeply sorry that it was so. I have to ask you to forgive the church for its failures.'

His companions looked surprised, though the Pilgrim Watcher understood. He had seen times of revival and times of decline without number. Revival had inevitably involved a clash with tradition, and repentance from dead works was an essential part of spiritual renewal.

Mr Christian continued, 'The sabbath concept is really part of God's welfare programme for his people. It's designed to refresh and renew us. Look, this is what I mean.

'The Lord has built rest into each day. In fact the biblical day started at six in the evening, so it wasn't long before everyone went to bed! God wants us to live a day at a time. Jesus said, "Do not be anxious about tomorrow, for tomorrow will be anxious for itself. Let the day's own trouble be sufficient for the day" (Matthew 6:34). Each day includes a period of rest in order to refresh us—but not quite enough. So from Creation the Lord ordained one day in seven as a break from ordinary labour so that all those "not quite" bits could be made up. But still not quite. So he added in holy days, or holidays, at different times throughout the year to make up those bits too. You could go on and have sabbath years every seven and even sabbaths of sabbath years every fifty in the Jubilee year. But you can see the point, can't you?'

They nodded.

'So you're saying Sunday should be a holiday?' asked the Courier.

'More or less. Though it doesn't have to be a Sunday particularly. Just one day off in seven from normal work. Russia tried to abolish the idea after the Revolution but found it didn't work. We attempted a seven day week in the munitions factories during the Second World War but found efficiency dropped. It's just something the Lord has built into us and our health suffers drastically if we don't take it. In fact, sometimes I feel the Lord permits Christians to be ill simply to catch up on their missed days off!'

'Does this mean, then, that people don't have to go to church on Sundays?' asked Mr Aquarius.

Mr Christian replied that being able to worship God with other Christians and hear his word is not a religious duty but a means of refreshment in itself, so it's a good thing to do on Sundays. Today, the Lord's people *enjoy* their fellowship and many spend a good part of their day together over meals or in the park or playing sport as an expression of the life of God's family. Gone are the days of simply endless meetings.

Jesus also taught by his own actions that Sunday is a day for doing acts of kindness to the poor and needy. He healed the sick and cast out demons on the sabbath, as well as enjoying walks in the countryside.

'It's a very new idea to me,' said the Courier. 'But it sounds good. Would I be right in saying that your approach springs out of a sabbath in your heart, so that you no longer feel the need to justify yourself by religious acts but can do all these things because you enjoy doing the will of God?'

'You're growing perceptive, Dai,' laughed Mr Christian. 'Sorry, Leo, but you can keep your meditation techniques. We've got something better.'

The latter mumbled incoherently into his beard. It was something about being more impressed if he saw the church actually being like that.

The doors of the church banged open at that moment and they turned as a clatter of tourists entered the building.

'Time to go, I think,' said the Pilgrim Watcher. And they agreed.

*   *   *

'When are you going to get a job, Dai?'

Mr Christian asked the question as they drank tea in the Courier's tumbledown flat. He twisted for a more comfortable position on the beat-out old sofa whilst the Welshman sought for an answer in his tea cup. He looked up.

'I've got a job, haven't I? I mean, I escort you round—
and others when I'm told.'

'And in the meantime you sit in this depressing room,
closeted from the outside world by piles of junk.' Mr
Christian indicated the jumble of odds and ends which
covered virtually every flat surface. 'Has Susan seen this
place yet?'

The Courier shook his head.

'Well, you need to do something, don't you?'

'Look now, I don't want to get like everyone around me.
I see these clockwork soldiers marching like automatons to
their businesses each day and marching back at the end.
Dead, grey lives, that's what they've got. Replace them
with computers and you'd hardly know the difference! I'm
a creative person, Peter; I *feel* things. How can I just work a
treadmill all day?'

Mr Christian was taken aback by the vehemence of the
Courier's feelings. He spoke gently. 'When did you last
work, Dai?'

'About four years ago. In an insurance office. Man, it
drove me scatty! About the most creative thing I could do
was to fill out forms in different coloured inks.'

'Did you leave or were you…um…made redundant?'

'No, I left but they would have sacked me anyway. I was
on the bottle, you see. I'm sure the job just made it worse.
Still I wasn't going to let them have the satisfaction of
giving me the boot…'

'So you booted yourself out.'

'I suppose so.'

Mr Christian then spoke to his friend about constructive
work being a part of God's wholeness. He reminded him
that both Jesus and Paul had done work. He was not
advocating some so-called 'protestant work ethic' in which
work is seen as a duty—a doctrine which suits capitalists
down to the ground. Nor could he agree with the socialists
who saw man as *homo faber*, discovering his dignity in his
labours by some co-operative sharing in its fruits. God was

neither a capitalist nor a communist.

'The Bible is realistic about work being hard,' he went on. 'Ever since the fall man has had to eke his existence from the earth. Futility is the lot of fallen man, whatever the economic system. You've found it in the sheer boredom of your work. Very few people have really exciting employment and even fewer are so wealthy that they don't need to work. A lot of people are cynical and despairing today as world recession, changing technology and government policies produce high unemployment and little choice. They are left with the option of the dole queue.'

He continued: 'The gospel gives a sense of purpose to work, not by first changing the social structures (though it does that as well) but by changing our attitude towards them. Here, pass me that Bible across, will you?'

He read from Ephesians 6:5–7: 'Slaves, be obedient to those who are your earthly masters, with fear and trembling, in singleness of heart, as to Christ; not in the way of eye-service, as men-pleasers, but as slaves of Christ, doing the will of God from the heart, rendering service with a good will as to the Lord and not to men.'

'Nobody was more repressed than the slave but Paul's counsel is not violent revolution but to serve the Master behind the master. Working to please Jesus is not a futile exercise; it releases us from purposelessness.'

'Does that mean the Bible endorses corrupt systems?' demanded the Courier.

'Not at all. Prophets like Isaiah, Amos and Hosea were fierce in their denunciation of social injustice. I believe the church must still speak out today against these evils.

'But the answer is found in the gospel, not in bloodshed. When both workers and employers turn to Christ things change radically. Read the little book of Philemon and you'll see what I mean.

'Although the prophets spoke specifically to God's covenant people, their appeal is based upon the character of God and, therefore, has application to all societies. Isaiah

5:16 says: "The Lord of hosts is exalted in justice, and the Holy God shows himself holy in righteousness". This has two important implications.

'First, justice only truly comes about through covenant. The answer to the world's unrighteous social structures is the preaching of the gospel. Only changed hearts can produce a changed society.

'Second, the church must come up with a viable economic system of its own which expresses righteousness and challenges existing systems by demonstrating that the gospel truly works. We need to recapture the testimony of the early church (in Acts 4:34) that "there was not a needy person among them" as an expression of our corporate wholeness.'

'So, what do I do meantime?'

'Seek the Lord for a job in which you can glorify him. Tell him about your creative desires and see what he brings up. Incidentally, Paul wrote to Timothy, "If anyone does not provide for his relatives…he has disowned the faith and is worse than an unbeliever" (1 Timothy 5:8). You may just have a relative to provide for soon!'

'Well, that's a good extra incentive, anyhow,' the Courier smiled. 'I'll take your advice and do something about it. By the way, do you think you could give me a hand clearing up this mess?'

Mr Christian chuckled. 'Serves me right, doesn't it? I've let myself in for that one. Well, where do we start?'

CHAPTER EIGHT

Food for Life

Grated carrot and cabbage, nuts, wholemeal cheese pizza, natural yoghurt and herb tea. Mr and Mrs Aquarius ate their picnic lunch with relish.

Next to them, Mr Christian and his wife, Zoë, were tucking into chicken drumsticks and mixed salad. They had brought along apples and brown rolls to go with it. And they drank coffee.

Susan sat with the Courier as he opened the bag he had prepared for both of them. Out came cold pork pies, jam sandwiches, cheese-and-onion crisps, chocolate biscuits and a flask of what turned out to be very sweet coffee. Dawn gazed at the pile with barely concealed disgust. Susan didn't look too happy either.

'I just don't know how you can eat that muck!' Dawn exclaimed. 'Goodness knows what it's doing to your insides.'

The three couples were sitting on the grass amidst the well-manicured flower gardens of Greenwich Park. The Pilgrim Watcher had perched himself in the branches of a great cedar tree nearby. He pricked up his ears and drew forth his writing case with a smile as the inevitable argument began.

'Here we go again,' Mr Christian laughed. 'Come on, what do you mean, Dawn?'

150

She shifted to a more comfortable position on the grass. 'I believe you are what you eat. What we put inside us doesn't only affect our physical health but our total well-being. If you start eating that sort of rubbish, Susan, you'll get all kinds of problems, never mind what this religion of yours says. I mean, look at it!'

The Courier viewed his offering dolefully and compared it with what the others were eating. He glanced at Susan and she reassured him with a smile.

'I don't mind,' she replied brightly. 'Dai prepared it with love and that's what really matters.'

Dawn snorted.

'Better is a dinner with herbs where love is than a fatted ox and hatred with it,' Mr Christian said, quoting from Proverbs 15:17.

'But that's begging the whole question,' Dawn cried. 'It wouldn't be so bad if he'd brought herbs and vegetables. I'd call that loving because it helps *produce* peace. All this meat, let alone this junk food, is half the cause of the tension and violence in our society. I'd say it was fuel for hatred.'

'Coo, that's a bit strong, isn't it?' Zoë challenged. 'Is that what you really mean when you say you are what you eat?'

Mr Aquarius wiped the crumbs from his beard and entered the discussion. 'It's a bit deeper than simply meat making us aggressive and herbs calming us down,' he explained. 'You see, wholeness is all to do with balance. Some foods, meats especially, are just so unbalanced that we won't eat them.'

'And this stuff which is mostly starch, sugar and chemical additives, we hesitate to call food at all,' Dawn interrupted disdainfully.

Zoë addressed Mr Aquarius politely. 'So when you talk about balance, do you mean something different from the right amounts of carbohydrates, proteins and fats?'

He nodded emphatically. 'Indeed I do. See, balance isn't just a chemical thing but it's spiritual too. Get the spiritual balance right and the chemical one follows automatically.

What you need is food which contains the correct positive and negative forces.'

Mr Aquarius proceeded to outline the theory of a macrobiotic diet. It has its origins in the Taoist principle that the universe consists of opposite but complementary forces. These are called *yin* and *yang*. Yin corresponds to acid and represents the feminine, passive principle. Yin foods include fruits, summer grown foods, those of expansive texture, green, blue or purple in colour, of sweet, sour and hot flavour. Yang, being the masculine, active principle, is represented by foods of animal origin, cereals and some vegetables. Foods which are compact and hard, red, orange or yellow in colour, of salty or bitter flavour and which ripen in autumn or winter are yang.

The most perfectly balanced food is the whole cereal and a macrobiotic diet will contain at least 50% of such. All foods are eaten in their natural form; refined and sugared foods hardly ever. Drinks are at a low level and salt intake is controlled. Vegetables from the nightshade family, such as potatoes and tomatoes, are rarely eaten.

'This sounds like your Ultimate Life Force again,' said the Courier through an unrepentant mouthful of pork pie.

Mr Aquarius agreed. 'When the balance is correct, energy or Ch'i as we call it, can flow properly through our beings. That means we live in health and at the same time give out good vibrations to those around us. Most illnesses occur because of an excess of yin or yang. Because Western diets are so unbalanced we get an unnecessary amount of illness.'

'Yes,' Dawn added. 'You see, processed foods like white flour have had the balance disturbed. That's why they're bad for you. And chemical additives are not only poisonous but upset the balance even further. That's why kids raised on junk-food diets are often hyperactive and troublesome. I think it's also the reason for diet-induced diseases like cancer, ulcers, colitis and diabetes.'

'Not forgetting all the psychological problems and crime and violence produced particularly by excess yang. If we all became vegetarians and ate this macrobiotic diet, I reckon we'd soon find ways for peaceful co-existence. That's one of the goals which we've got, anyway,' her husband concluded.

Susan turned to Mr Christian who was lying on his back in the sun, chewing on a blade of grass.

'What do you think of all this, Peter?' she asked.

He opened his eyes and sat up. 'Not a lot really. I don't believe in this Ultimate Life Force; I believe in the living God. And there are no contradictory principles in him that need holding in balance—he's just pure goodness. So I'm not happy with any food theory, however healthy it looks, if its roots are based in deception. As I think I've said before, replacing the living God with a blind Force is one of the subtle deceits of this age.'

Zoë smiled. Her husband always rose to the bait!

He took a Bible from his pocket and read from Mark 7:18–21, '"Do you not see that whatever goes into a man is from outside cannot defile him, since it enters, not his heart but his stomach, and so passes on?" (Thus he declared all foods clean.) And he said, "What comes out of a man is what defiles a man. For from within, out of the heart of man, come evil thoughts..."' He closed the book and continued.

'What Jesus is saying is that neither the kind of food nor the way you eat it is of any moral or spiritual importance,' he explained. 'Evil behaviour springs from evil hearts. When we're irritable, angry, restless or whatever, it's because we're sinful creatures and God's remedy for that isn't a new diet but a new heart. No yin-yang food regimen is going to solve either our personal problems or those of the world at large. Only the blood of Jesus and the power of the Holy Spirit can truly change human nature. Whether you choose to live on pork chops, raw carrots or chocolate biscuits all your life will make not the slightest difference.'

'Hear, hear!' cried the Courier as he munched his choc-bar.

'That doesn't mean some diets aren't better than others,' Mr Christian hastily added, looking at the Courier with mock sternness. 'But more of that later, maybe.'

'It's a long time since I read the Bible,' said Dawn urbanely. 'But I seem to remember reading quite a lot about food in it. Weren't Adam and Eve vegetarians? Oh, and Daniel also? You say it doesn't matter, but aren't you contradicting your own holy book?'

He replied, 'It's true that the early members of the human race were vegetarians, right up to the Flood, in fact, but that had no bearing on their moral condition. Actually those vegetarians were very evil people. That's why the Flood came. So it's no use thinking we'll all regain innocence by not eating meat. Anyway, after the Flood, God told the survivors that it was all right to eat meat. He wouldn't have said that if it was harmful to us, would he?'

'I suppose not,' she answered airily. 'But why make the change after the Flood, anyway? Not that I believe in it, of course,' she added quickly.

'It's difficult to say, really,' he replied slowly. 'Maybe the Flood had reduced the fertility of the earth so that it was necessary to eat animals from then on. I don't know. But, anyway, the time after the Flood was a new era and I guess lots of things changed.

'Whatever the reason, the important thing is that there's no moral guilt attached to eating meat. I know you don't like this Dawn, but your whole position is one which seeks human salvation apart from the death of Jesus. What you've got to do, sooner or later, is identify with him in his gory physical crucifixion for your sins. Jesus said, "Unless you eat the flesh of the Son of Man and drink his blood, you have no life in you" ' (John 6:53).

'You know, I find that really offensive, don't you?' She spoke with quiet intensity.

'So did many in his day. But it's the only way you'll ever be truly whole.'

That rather put paid to the conversation for a while and a few minutes later Mr and Mrs Aquarius said they were going for a stroll. After they had left, Susan had a question.

'I'm sorry to keep on about this, Peter, but I'm sure I've read somewhere in the New Testament that it's all right for a believer to be a vegetarian.'

Mr Christian said that was so. In Romans 14, Paul tackles a problem which had come up in the young church. One of the characteristics of early Christian fellowship was that they enjoyed many meals together. Which was fine, provided you could agree about what to eat. The difficulty arose with regard to meat.

Not that anyone thought eating meat was sinful of itself or was worried about the suffering of animals or their own health expectancy. It all revolved around the fact that meat sold by pagan butchers was first dedicated to idols, behind which were demons. Would a believer be spiritually contaminated by eating such meat? Some thought so. Paul calls these 'weaker brethren'. He and others had more robust consciences over the issue and considered that the meat was only unclean if you thought it was unclean. There was no absolute moral principle involved.

Hence, dietary considerations must not be a divisive issue. Christians must not despise one another because of their different eating habits. Nor must they pressurize each other to go against their consciences. That would be sin, "For whatever does not proceed from faith is sin" (Romans 14:23). These lesser matters must never take precedence over more important things. 'For the kingdom of God does not mean food and drink but righteousness and peace and joy in the Holy Spirit; he who thus serves Christ is acceptable to God and approved by men' (Romans 14:17–18).

'So, it's not really an issue we face today? At least, not in the West,' said Susan.

'No, but the principle is a very important one,' Mr Christian pointed out. 'Satan is always trying to divide believers over petty issues. He does it by making them seem bigger than they really are. That could happen over the wholefoods thing at the moment, for example. A lot of Christians, especially the more middle class ones, are getting into the healthy eating trip and it's only a small step to judging those who haven't got "enlightenment" on the subject. I've even heard people describing wholefoods as "kingdom food"—which is absolute nonsense, of course. Or you get this superior attitude, "Oh, we *never* touch white bread". And so on.'

'A bit like Dawn over there,' the Courier interjected.

'Mm,' he agreed. 'We're never far from the danger of that legalistic spirit.'

'Wasn't that what happened in New Testament times?' Zoë queried. 'I mean, there was a lot of legalism about then, wasn't there?'

'How do you mean?' asked Susan.

'Well, those who said you had to keep the Old Testament food laws if you were going to be a complete believer,' she replied. 'It wasn't enough just to believe on Jesus. You needed some "works" as well, to be truly saved.'

'Yes, but it went a bit deeper than that,' her husband continued. 'These people understood that Christianity had sprung from Jewish roots and that Gentiles had to become part of Israel in order to be saved. The trouble was, they misunderstood what that meant.

'If I can put it simply, they thought that being part of Israel meant having the faith of Abraham and following the Law of Moses. Paul's great contention was that the true Israel is *only* of the faith of Abraham. The Law is fulfilled in Christ; so it just isn't applicable to those who have the Spirit. All we need is Christ. That's the message of Galatians.

'To add the Law, or any part of it, to the work of grace eventually distorts the message until it becomes a false gospel. Imposing dietary rules, whether Old Testament ones or any current crazes, makes us slaves to "the elemental spirits of the universe". The moment we start attributing our behaviour or spiritual calibre to the kind of food we eat, we fall into this trap. In 1 Timothy 4, Paul describes such food prohibitions as nothing less than a "doctrine of demons". He says: "For everything created by God is good, and nothing is to be rejected if it is received with thanks-giving" (1 Timothy 4:4).'

'I feel very happy with that,' declared the Courier, speaking through a mouthful of crisps. 'Anybody want one?'

They looked at him in despair and burst out laughing together.

'No thanks,' said Susan. 'But I'll have one of Peter and Zoë's apples if you don't mind.'

*　　*　　*

'You know, I don't think you've been very honest about what you eat.'

Dawn made the mild accusation after surveying the cupboards in Mr and Mrs Christian's kitchen. The Courier and Susan had gone off for a walk together. The Pilgrim Watcher had vanished but not before saying he had someone for Mr and Mrs Christian to meet later that day. Mr Christian had felt a bit bad about upsetting Dawn so they had invited the couple back for a drink. Their quizzical response to her charge invited an explanation.

'Well, you seemed to be defending Dai's awful eating habits this lunch time and more or less saying our ideas were worthless. But I can see from your larder that you live on a very healthy diet yourselves. I mean, look, you eat wholemeal bread. You cook with brown flour, brown rice, brown sugar. You've got tons of herbs and spices. Your breakfast cereals are all wholewheat. Then there's this soya margarine and the corn oil.'

She glanced out of the window at the garden. 'Ha, and you even grow your own fruit and vegetables!'

'Yes, but we've got a freezer full of meat, too,' Mr Christian protested mildly. 'And we eat jam and biscuits—as well as drinking gallons of coffee.'

'Well, you've got a way to go,' she replied. 'But come off it, Peter, by and large you're living on a very healthy wholefood diet that's not so very far removed from ours.

You don't actually agree with eating the rubbish Dai eats, do you? So what are you really getting at?'

The couple exchanged glances, then laughed.

'Fair enough,' Mr Christian answered cheerfully. 'You deserve an explanation. But first, what'll you have to drink?'

He opened a cupboard.

'We can offer you cinnamon tea, fennel, peppermint, lemon…'

'What?' cried Dawn. 'I don't believe it.' She paused. 'Well I'll have fennel, if you don't mind.'

When they were sitting down in the front room, Dawn pressed her question on them again. Mr Christian sipped his coffee.

'There's no catch in it really,' he said. 'We do genuinely believe that some diets are better than others. We happen to think that the average British diet is not very healthy so, over the years, we've changed our eating habits for something better.'

'But that's just for our bodies' sake,' his wife added. 'We honestly don't think our diet has got any moral or spiritual benefit. So we wouldn't press it on anyone else. I think that's where we differ from you—as well as disagreeing about some of the foods which are all right to eat, of course.'

'So is what you eat entirely divorced from your spiritual life? A sort of secular zone?' Mr Aquarius asked.

'No it's not,' Mr Christian replied quickly. 'We don't believe that any part of our life should be secular. Biblical Christianity is an all-embracing thing and God's presence gives everything a spiritual dimension.'

'I'm getting confused,' Dawn complained. 'One moment you're saying food isn't spiritually important; the next, it is.'

'Right, well, let's explain what we mean,' Mr Christian replied. 'As you know, we want to live in wholeness. Now, from our point of view, that's got its origins in Christ. It starts on the inside as we come to share his nature. But it's got a physical dimension too, because knowing the Lord has quite a profound effect on our general health. And that's tied up with the positive outlook which our faith produces.'

'So how does that affect your choice of food?' Mr Aquarius asked.

'Well, we aren't passive about life. Do you remember when we were discussing stress some time ago? We felt much of the trouble with society is its sheer apathy and passivity. People sit back and expect things to work out rather than taking positive action for themselves. At least you and I are agreed that we have to do something if we want health and wholeness.

'Now our faith in Jesus produces a sense of responsibility in us,' he continued. 'It began when we took responsibility for our sins, but it continues as an active response to God's grace and his promises. I happen to believe the Lord promises health so I act as a healthy person. That includes eating food which is appropriate to healthy people. Now we don't need lists of authorized foods or texts to do that—just sanctified common sense.'

Mr Aquarius nodded. 'I think I understand what you're saying. So you've got a spiritual motive, which most people lack, for your self-preservation?'

'I don't see it quite that way,' Zoë came in. 'It sounds too self-centred. I believe my body is a temple of the Holy Spirit. It doesn't just belong to me any more; it's the Lord's. Now I'm not denying that self-preservation isn't a strong motive when it comes to looking after myself. After all, that's why we look out when we cross the road. But I've got this higher motive as well, you see; I want to look after my body so that it can serve him. At least, as much as I have control over that.'

'Yes,' added her husband. 'There are some things we seem unable to do anything about. That's in the mystery of God's will. But where we have a choice, as we do with food, we want to do what's best for God's temple.'

'You talk about sanctified common sense. How has that

affected your thinking about food?' Dawn enquired.

'Well, we try to avoid faddiness,' Zoë replied. 'For example, a lot of people these days seem to think that tea is less harmful than coffee, but actually tea contains more or less the same amounts of caffeine as coffee, as well as a lot of tannin. So maybe coffee is the better of the two. I also prefer it! But we drink herb teas as well so that our caffeine intake isn't too high. I read somewhere that caffeine hinders calcium assimilation as well as destroying some vitamin C, so there may be something to be said for drinking decaffeinated coffee and avoiding cola drinks.' She shrugged her shoulders.

'Or there's this fad of putting bran in everything to increase the roughage,' Mr Christian chipped in. 'I'm not saying people who live on a lot of processed food don't need to do something about the lack of fibre in their diet. But a tablespoon or so a day of simple miller's bran is quite enough to keep most of those folk regular and reduce their risk of contracting diverticulitis or bowel cancer.'

'It's begging the question though, isn't it?' Dawn interrupted. 'If people ate a more natural diet they wouldn't be short of fibre in the first place. I must say it annoys me when I hear bran treated as a cure-all medicine for problems no one need have to start with. And as for all these commercial varieties of sugared bran...'

'I agree,' Mr Christian interjected with a laugh at Dawn's intensity. 'Incidentally, we know someone who used to eat a lot of bran breakfast cereal and it actually made her constipated because she just wasn't drinking the vast amount of liquid it required to get through her system. So you've got to keep a balance.

'Can I mention another "in thing"?' he continued. 'I'm thinking of honey. Some people claim it's better than sugar —especially the dreaded white stuff! But honey is only sugar with impurities. It's the same with brown sugar. The whole question revolves around how much mineral value there is in those impurities and how much you'd need to

consume in order to get any significant benefit. The reason
we eat brown sugar, by the way, is because we prefer the
taste and texture. But too much of *any* sugar just isn't good
for us.'

'Actually there's a warning about honey in the Bible,'
Zoë added. 'It says, "It is not good to eat much honey"
(Proverbs 25:27). They knew even then that overindulgence
in sweet stuff is harmful. So I try to avoid buying foods
loaded with honey, sugar, glucose syrup or dextrose.'

People on high-sugar diets—and the British are some of
the world's worst—tend to be overweight and suffer all the
attendant diseases. Because sugar is a readily available
energy source to the body, it discourages the metabolizing
of fats and starches into fuel, with the result that these get
stored around the body as fat reserves. Bad teeth are largely
caused by the parental habit of indulging children with
sweets. In later years high sugar consumers are particularly
prone to diabetes.

Because sugar is nice to taste, manufacturers tend to add
it to many foods simply to boost sales. It's worth reading
the label first! Many soft drinks are little more than sugar
syrup with chemical flavourings—and the low-calorie ones
are just chemical flavourings! A lot of mousse-type desserts
are simply sugar, starch and chemicals. Sweets are almost
entirely sugar.

'We cook most of our own food because we can control
how much sugar goes in,' said Zoë. 'And I've found that
I've been able to gradually wean the family away from its
love of sweet things, so we use far less than most people.'

Mr Christian explained that the use of fresh foods rather
than canned or packaged foods was also an important
aspect of their diet. Processing destroys most vitamins and
beneficial enzymes as well as harming the texture and taste
of the product. Much factory-processing of food requires
the use of nutrient destroying techniques along with the
addition of chemical preservatives and colourants. Zoë felt
it was largely laziness and badly-balanced lifestyles which

made so many people opt for convenience foods. Lack of time to cook properly is usually caused by a misplaced set of priorities, she felt. It is also considerably cheaper to prepare your own food and it tastes infinitely better than shop bought stuff.

'So you think Christians should avoid additives?' enquired Dawn.

'Yes, as far as possible,' Zoë replied. 'There are so many these days, something like three thousand compared with a hundred at the turn of the century, I believe. Many of them seem unnecessary, especially the colourings. I'm sure they don't do us any good. But if you cook for yourself you hardly need to have them anyway.'

Mr and Mrs Christian also stressed the value of eating wholemeal bread and cereals. Processed white flour has anything from half of all the vitamins and trace elements removed, and only some are replaced. Wholemeal, as opposed to wheatmeal (a dubious term for something in between), contains all the vitamins and minerals as well as the bran. The latter is very important for health. It helps prevent the bowel disorder, diverticulitis. It also speeds up the movement of food through the bowels, preventing the formation of poisons. There is considerable evidence that constipation allows toxins to affect the colon and these can cause cancer. Eating wholemeal food could virtually eliminate these complaints.

Foods with plenty of roughage absorb more water and tend to bulk in the stomach, giving that satisfying full feeling without the need to overeat. They are also good for teeth and gums because they require more chewing. In addition to whole cereals, raw or lightly cooked fresh vegetables come into this category.

'I know we're not going to agree about meat,' said Mr Aquarius. 'Because we've already talked about that. But, I mean, do you really believe it's good for you?'

'I don't think it's bad for us.' Mr Christian answered. 'But I think that in the West we eat far more than we should. I had a friend come over from India recently and I was amazed when he described English food as too strong. I had experienced some of his wife's curries when I was out there, and I thought those were strong! So I asked him what he meant. He said it was the meat. He ate meat about once a week, whereas we in this country eat it at almost every meal. That's what he meant by too strong.'

'Too much yang,' said Dawn impishly.

'No, he was a Christian. I think he was making a good point. We do eat far more animal protein than is necessary. One of the effects that has is to drastically increase our fat intake and that's harmful to our hearts and arteries. With just a little imagination, we can just as easily, and much more cheaply, eat more vegetable proteins in the form of beans. That's what we're tending to do anyway.'

'One last question and then we must be going,' said Mr Aquarius. 'Do you take vitamin supplements?'

'Yes, at times,' he replied. 'Though the debate about their effectiveness is wide open at present. Nobody can be conclusive about whether the body is actually capable of utilizing vitamins when they are taken in this way, or whether they mostly just pass straight through us. In any case, because we eat a wholesome diet we don't see the need for vast supplements.'

'So what do you take?' asked Dawn.

'Oh, in the winter some extra vitamin C, and the B complex as well as a little iron. We get adequate amounts of vitamins A, D and E, and too much A and D is harmful, anyway. We feel better for it but wouldn't want to go overboard about it, as some seem to.'

'Nevertheless, many women would cope with their monthly cycles much better if they took B vitamins and iron a week or two before they were due,' Zoë chipped in. 'They definitely seem to make it easier to cope. Though I believe the real secret of handling the pressures of pre-menstrual tension lies in prayer,' she added.

Dawn opened her mouth to protest, but at that moment

her husband rose. 'Well thanks for the tea. It makes a change to find we've something in common, even if we're there for different reasons. Incidentally, are you going to teach Dai all this, since he seems to have become one of your disciples?'

'I think he'll pick it up,' Mr Christian replied with a smile. 'But, as I said earlier, we won't force it on anyone. It's not *that* important to us. I suspect Susan will influence him for the better, anyhow.'

'Just mind it's not the other way round,' Dawn retorted. 'I still feel a concern for that girl, you know.'

Mr Christian smiled blandly but said nothing.

*   *   *

Mr and Mrs Christian met the Pilgrim Watcher at MacDonalds in Bromley. Sitting next to him was a simply enormous woman in her early thirties whom he introduced as Michelle. They waited until Mr Christian produced a couple of cheeseburgers and milk shakes.

'I don't think Leo and Dawn would be too happy with this, do you?' he said on returning.

'I'm sure they wouldn't,' his wife laughed. 'But actually it's a fairly well-balanced meal, you know.'

They turned to the Pilgrim Watcher for an explanation as to why they were there.

'I am not allowed to do this very often,' he said. 'But Michelle is a desperate believer. She has been crying out to the Most High for help and I have been permitted to appear to her and arrange this meeting.'

They smiled at Michelle.

'I don't know what's happening,' she began. 'I didn't know angels could do this. Anyway here I am and, yes, I do need help.'

'What's your problem?' asked Mr Christian.

'What's my problem? Well, look at me. I'm fat, that's what; really fat, and I hate it, and I hate myself.'

'But you're a believer?' Zoë enquired.

'Yes I gave my life to the Lord about five years ago. And I love the Lord, I really do. But I'm fed up with being like this. See, I just can't stop eating.'

They surveyed the pile of cartons in front of her and nodded. Michelle really did have a problem.

'Yes, I've done the lot. Low fat, calorie controlled, F-plan, Weight Watchers, quick ones, slow ones, you name it and I've tried it. And none of 'em work.'

A few more questions ascertained that Michelle was basically a comfort-eater. Her parents had separated when she was seven and following that traumatic time her mother had indulged her with food, with the result that whenever she felt low she now turned to eating for help.

As in so many similar cases, Michelle had put on weight and had gradually come to despise and reject herself. This made her feel almost continually depressed, which in its turn led her to seek more comfort in food...and she put on more weight. A vicious spiral. No amount of dieting was going to help Michelle because she was increasing her pain by depriving herself of her one means of comfort every time she tried. Her real problem was inner.

'We don't believe in all this dieting,' said Mr Christian. 'Actually it's sheer legalism; a whole lot of rules and regulations that you try to impose on yourself. All it is, really, is self-punishment. God doesn't want his people to live like that.'

Michelle was interested. 'Well, no one's ever told me that before. My Christian friends just say: "You need to go on a diet." And, "If you lost weight you'd feel better." Course I would but I can't, can I?'

Mr and Mrs Christian shared their approach with her. They thought she probably needed some ministry to deal with her past but she had to prepare herself first. So they counselled her to recognize her true identity in Christ.

Every believer, fat or thin, pretty or ugly, tall or short, is a new creation in Christ. Each of us is fully accepted by him and precious in his sight. Revelation 2:17 promises the conquerors 'hidden manna' and 'A white stone, with a new name written on the stone which no one knows except him who receives it.' For each of us God has an inner supply of food and a personal identity. They counselled Michelle to seek the Lord until she had come to recognize her 'new name' for herself. That alone would provide sufficient inner motivation to be different; it would supply her with the necessary dignity and self-worth.

'When you've reached that point, you'll be in a position to repent,' said Mr Christian. 'You see, basically overeating is the sin of gluttony.'

'Yes, I know. I'm a greedy pig,' Michelle interrupted angrily. Tears came to her eyes. 'That's what they all say.'

Zoë calmed her down. 'No, Peter isn't calling you a greedy pig. That's what you're saying about yourself,' she continued gently. 'What the sin of gluttony really is, is feeding on the wrong things. I don't mean cream buns and chocolates, but using physical food instead of spiritual food.

'Look, there's a verse which helped me once. It's Jesus speaking. He says, "My food is to do the will of him who sent me" (John 4:34). Serving the Lord is truly nourishing. It fills the gap and satisfies the hunger. What you need to repent from, Michelle, is letting ordinary food try to do that. It never can. All that happens is you get fat.'

They explained to her how to feed on the word of God, which Psalm 19:10 describes as 'sweeter also than honey and drippings of the honeycomb'. Reading the Scriptures instead of turning to food is a vital key to healing for people with Michelle's problem.

She agreed with all they had said and promised she would try to do it.

'But I've still got to lose this weight somehow, haven't I? What do I do if I don't diet?'

'Well, obviously you've got to eat differently and we can give you some practical advice on that,' said Mr Christian. 'But, you see, the important thing is to get right on the inside. Do that and your secondary problem, your weight, will begin to take care of itself.

'What really matters,' Zoë explained, 'is not how much weight you lose in a week or month but whether you are significantly slimmer in a year or so. That'll only come about as your inner attitudes change and they lead to a reform in your eating habits.'

Mr and Mrs Christian commended their own approach to eating. They counselled her not to eat between meals but whenever she felt hungry to go and do something for the Lord. When she felt low, she should go and bless somebody else, visit a friend, help a neighbour, perhaps write a letter. They advised her to wean herself off sugar as much as possible and to reduce her overall fat intake by eating less meat, cheese and fried stuff. Even these adjustments dramatically reduce the daily calorie intake and allow the body's metabolism to function more healthily. They also commended some regular exercise which itself would raise her metabolic rate and encourage healthy weight-loss.

'You've given me hope,' she said, 'I feel much better already. I'm going to give it a try.'

She turned to thank the Pilgrim Watcher for arranging the chat, but he had gone.

'Oh, I didn't see him go. Is he always like that? And is he really an angel?'

Mr and Mrs Christian smiled.

*   *   *

As they walked home together they pondered the subject of food.

'You know, we live in a crazy world,' said Mr Christian. 'Here we are with folk like Michelle who are trapped by over-indulgence, forever failing to diet. Then you've got others who go completely the other way and get anorexia. They get trapped by successful dieting!'

'Yes, it's awful,' his wife agreed. 'I think you're right

when you put it down to legalism and satanic bondage. It really is.'

'If the Son shall make you free, you shall be free indeed.' He pondered the saying. 'Liberated from sin, from Satan, from death and hell. Free from striving to save ourselves by trying to keep the rules. It's glorious, isn't it? All that's necessary is to trust in Jesus and do what he says. It's so simple really.'

She snuggled close to him. 'Yes, that's what wholeness is all about, darling.'

CHAPTER NINE

Joyful Simplicity

Life is very hard for the rich. It is also very hard for the poor. Perhaps this is why Agur asked, 'Give me neither poverty nor riches' (Proverbs 30:8). Finding that elusive balance, that simplicity of life, is a part of the quest for Christian wholeness and an essential element of true conversion.

The Pilgrim Watcher was reading the newspaper with great interest. He looked up at Mr Christian.

'You know, many of your politicians and leaders are greatly deluded,' he said.

'Probably,' the other replied. 'But how do you mean?'

'They are possessed with the notion that the state of the economy has brought about the ills of the nation. The political factions dispute together over the means whereby peace can come about, but all of them agree that if the economy comes right then everything else will go well. Do they not perceive the error in their thinking?'

'I guess not,' Mr Christian answered. 'But that's the problem of living in a materialistic society. We've decided that all we've got is what we can see, produce and possess, so anything which gives us more of it is good. And anything which reduces our purchasing power is bad. It's called improving our standard of living.'

'It is more akin to the standard of dying,' the Pilgrim Watcher muttered. 'Do you remember the words of the Lord: "Beware of covetousness: for a man's life consisteth not in the abundance of the things which he possesseth" (Luke 12:15 AV)? That destroys the foundation on which your society is built.'

Mr Christian responded readily. 'I know. And it's one of the great challenges facing all who truly wish to be disciples of Jesus. How do we practically produce an alternative society based on spiritual values and free from the cancer of covetousness?'

The Pilgrim Watcher asked Mr Christian if he felt most believers had a real commitment to live free from this burden of materialism. He was told that many had blindly accepted the values of the world around them and spent almost as much of their time and energy as the non-Christians in buying, exchanging, servicing, mending, improving and serving their possessions. The influence of the belly god is far-reaching.

'I believe we need releasing from this wretched possession-serving mentality,' he said. 'It cripples the church and keeps many saints in a state of continuous unhealth. This morning I read something about it in Paul's letter to Timothy. Here, let me see if I can find it.'

He picked up a Bible and read, 'The love of money is the root of all evils; it is through this craving that some have wandered away from the faith and pierced their hearts with many pangs' (1 Timothy 6:10).

'Greed leads people away from the Lord,' he continued. 'It first distracts us, and then becomes a cruel taskmaster. We live in a world where the poor are dispossessed but the rich are possessed by their possessions. They just can't stop consuming. That's sick! You know Jesus said, "You *cannot* serve God and mammon" (Matthew 6:24).'

He described again how, years before, he had coveted a motorbike—because his brother had got one. In spite of all the Lord's gentle warnings, he eventually acquired it. And, true to form, began to use it for the Lord's work. That eased the conscience.

'The crunch came, quite literally, a couple of years later,' he recalled. 'At the time I had the bike plastered in stickers advertising a Billy Graham crusade. Then I wrapped it around a tree one night. I'll never forget the humiliation of pushing that twisted wreck home the next day, still covered in stickers! God spoke to me very sternly. He said, "You cannot justify your idols by painting my name over them!" It was a painful lesson.'

'You were blessed that the Most High made it so clear to you,' the Pilgrim Watcher replied. 'Not everyone perceives that his desire for these things is idolatry. Did you ever purchase another bike?'

'As a matter of fact, yes. But this time I really prayed and waited until the Lord directed me. That was altogether different.'

The Lord is not opposed to his people having possessions, provided these are clearly in his will and truly serve the purposes of his kingdom. What he does object to is us simply following the crowd and buying things because "everyone has one these days". *All* our money is his, not just the offering. Consequently, we must ask him what he wants done with it. This does not mean we will live in some false frugality, nor does it mean excessive luxury. God's will for us is simplicity, an uncluttered lifestyle flowing from an uncluttered heart. It does not mean that all believers will have the same material standard of living but it does mean we will be freed from the burden and distraction of our possessions.

As Mr Christian was thinking about this, the front door bell rang and he went to answer it. A few seconds later he ushered in a fellow called Len.

"Allo, pleased ter meet yer,' he said cheerily upon being introduced. 'Sorry ter disturb yer. I only popped round ter borrow 'is wheelbarra. Oh, and ter give yer back yer batt'ry charger,' he said to Mr Christian.

'Please be seated,' the Pilgrim Watcher invited. 'Do you borrow many things in your church?'

'Can't stop long,' he replied taking up the offer. 'Oh, yeah, well, I mean, we all do it, don't we? It's wot bein' in the family's all about—this sharin' lark. I mean, there's no sense in me buyin' a wheelbarra if 'e's got one now, is there? Much cheaper bein' a Christian, yer know!'

'Len's quite right,' Mr Christian explained. 'We do have an enormous amount of sharing in our community. Anything from wheelbarrows to cars or babyclothes. A lot of our people go on holiday together, too. Sometimes those who have bigger houses loan them to those with council flats while they're on holiday. Some families share ownership of washing machines or freezers. Others with a bit of capital make interest free loans or gifts to help folk buy houses. A good number of single folk share flats together. Actually, the list is endless; as varied as life itself.'

'Yeah, we share just about everything—except our wives, of course,' Len joked.

'I am glad to hear it,' was the Pilgrim Watcher's dry reply.

Mr Christian explained that one of the key principles to living simply is renouncing ownership. He quoted Acts 4:32, 'Now the company of those who believed were of one heart and soul, and no one said that any of the things which he possessed was his own, but they had everything in common.' He said they didn't think this necessarily meant living in communes, with a common purse, but it does mean seeing everything as a means of serving God and his people. Instead of saying, 'It's mine and nobody's going to touch it', which is the world's mentality, believers see that possessions are a gift from God for the common good, even though, inevitably, in practice some things are fairly exclusively used by one person. It is the fundamental heart attitude which is all-important if this is going to work in practice.

'Well, must toddle on,' said Len. 'Can't sit 'ere all day.

Got a load of rubble ter shift. Nice meetin' yer. Cheers!'

And with that he was off.

'He's quite a character,' said Mr Christian when he had gone. The Pilgrim Watcher agreed. He had another question.

'How do you understand the Lord's command to forsake everything in order to be a disciple? You remember that he bade the rich young ruler go and sell everything he possessed and give it away to the poor.'

Mr Christian pondered a moment before replying.

'There are those who teach that Jesus meant this literally for every follower and those who take it that way often have fine testimonies of God's provision for their needs. But the problem with saying it applies like this to everyone is that the New Testament church didn't interpret it that way. Sure, in the early days they sold off excess possessions and produced some kind of common pool of goods, but they didn't make themselves destitute to a man even then. After all, they were still able to meet and break bread from house to house, so they must've still had houses—or at least the rent for them.'

Mr Christian felt it was unrealistic for all believers to possess nothing. However radical Jesus was, he never lacked reality and his commands can be applied in any society and at any time in history without being nonsensical. What he was really driving at was the need for us to shake off our dependence upon material things so that we can be truly free to follow him. We have to learn to be indifferent to the things by which the world sets so much store.

'For many, the only way to enter this happy simplicity will be by actually selling everything and starting again with God,' he continued. 'That's especially true for those who are wealthy at the time of their conversion. Jesus said it was exceedingly difficult for a rich man to enter the kingdom of God.

'It's false teaching to say, "All you need to do is be born again" and then let these "converts" go back to living the same old affluent lifestyle, only this time with Jesus. To enter the kingdom requires more radical surgery than that! Until the cancer is removed there can be no true healing.'

'Simplicity,' he said, 'is where we learn the reality of faith and the wonder of God's provision. It teaches us a right perspective on worldly wealth and the importance of keeping a light hold on it. That's the only way we can safely handle God's abundance when it comes.

'Paul testified that he had learned how to be content in both abundance and want. He was not disturbed by either, because his fundamental source of peace was in the Lord himself. The greatest gain he knew was godliness with contentment—beyond that he asked for nothing more than food and clothing (1 Timothy 6:6–8).

'The moment our peace and satisfaction depends upon our possessions we've moved out of God's wholeness,' he concluded.

The Pilgrim Watcher was profoundly disturbed by the relative wealth of the Western world compared with the rest of the world. Something like seventy million people live on the brink of death by starvation and over four hundred million suffer chronic malnutrition as well as inadequate medical care. Meanwhile, the affluent West demands an ever-increasing standard of material comfort, at the direct expense of the poor.

They agreed that as the church was restored in spiritual power and influence some radical stance would need to be taken towards the whole problem and many people were turning their attention to these issues of justice. 'Riches at others' expense' is the maxim of the godless West. The church must renounce that mentality and preach a gospel inextricably linked to social change. 'Let me share my bread with you' must be the new heart attitude.

'I believe one of the real keys to maintaining joyful simplicity lies in being a giver,' said Mr Christian. 'Giving not only provides the much needed resources for God's work, but it releases us from spending our excess income on an ever-increasing number of possessions and self-indulgences. That keeps us healthy and trim.'

The Pilgrim Watcher agreed and reminded him of Paul's words to Timothy concerning the rich. 'They are to do good, to be rich in good deeds, liberal and generous' (1 Timothy 6:17–18).

'It is no sin for you to obtain wealth by righteous means,' he said. 'But it is sin to live as the rich of this world, in selfish indulgence and indifference to those who are in need. The cure for this affliction is to give.'

'That's right,' said Mr Christian. 'Tithing is not enough! It's all too easy to salve our consciences because we fulfil some "commitment" requirement. The Lord's call is to a cheerful, generous and sacrificial giving which puts us in the position of having to trust God for our needs—just like our poorer brethren across the world. We must keep free from "the deceitfulness of riches" if we really want to be whole.

'There's a tremendous promise in 2 Corinthians 9:8. I expect you know it.' He went on, and quoted: ' "God is able to provide you with every blessing in abundance, so that you may always have enough of everything and may provide in abundance for every good work." I really believe that's the reason why the Lord wants his people to prosper, especially in this country. As I've said before, we suffer from a poverty spirit. Low expectation. That's one of the reasons why everything's so small and struggling in lots of churches and why we can do so little for the poor.'

'Yes, the Lord wants a work worthy of his great name,' affirmed the Pilgrim Watcher. 'That means you needs must become men and women of great faith. Put to death this poverty spirit; it is of the Enemy!'

'I agree. We need faith for a mighty release of resources, not so that we can live in the lap of luxury but so we can really bless the needy about us. God can meet our needs sufficiently so that we're at peace ourselves *and* he can provide ample resources for the work of the kingdom.

'One of the greatest sins of evangelicalism, to my mind, is the way it associates the gospel with middle class affluence. That is especially happening in the States where many evangelicals seem increasingly allied to right wing government and the values of "the American way of life". But this country isn't free from it. Most evangelistic outreach still takes place amongst the middle class to the neglect of the poor. One of the confirmations of Jesus' messiahhood was that "the poor have good news preached to them" (Luke 7:22). Whenever the church is truly revived that is an inevitable result.

'If God's people had taken this seriously in times past, I don't think Karl Marx would have been able to justify his alternative religion of Communism. He saw the church largely identified with political power and the prestige of the rich. The very people who should have been fighting the injustice had become a cause of it. Would that he had put his energies and vision into the kingdom of God—but he never found the radical church.

'Communism has proved not to be the answer. It's a secularized Old Testament legalism and can only replace one bondage with another. I want radicals to see that true freedom lies in the grace of God and a people committed to that. Socialism says, "You've got to share with me what you've got—or I'll make you!" Grace says, "I would like to share what God has given me with you".'

'The people of this age are in most desperate need of grace,' declared the Pilgrim Watcher.

'I believe it's coming,' replied Mr Christian with quiet certainty.

*　　*　　*

I've never seen so much junk! Do you really need all this stuff?'

Susan had, at last, been invited back to the Courier's flat. In spite of his efforts at tidying up, the place still resembled a scrap heap. He surveyed the scene morosely.

'I'm just a collector, I suppose. I keep things in case they'll come in handy.'

'Including a pair of glasses with one lens, a birdcage with no bottom and a tin of cat food with no cat!' she exclaimed.

'Well, if I get really hungry…'

'Dai!'

She put her head on one side and smiled wistfully.

'I do love you,' she said and rushed over to give him a hug. 'But what are we going to do with all this? I'll never find you underneath it all, let alone anything else.'

He held her at arm's length and gazed steadily into her clear blue eyes for a long moment.

'I love you, too,' he whispered at last.

Susan smiled. Her eyes sparkled. Then they hugged each other tightly with that unique joy which comes upon knowing that the love you feel is returned and a future together is assured.

'We must get engaged,' cried the Courier. 'I'll sell all this to buy a ring. What trivia! What passing fancies! What vanity! It all fades to dull ashes before the burning brightness of love. No longer do I need your false security, you worthless trinkets!'

He swept his arm around the room, eyes blazing with passion. Susan burst out laughing at this sudden burst of Welsh eloquence.

'Not so fast,' she cried. 'Girls need a little more time, you know. You mad Welshman!'

By the time ten minutes had elapsed, they were in a slightly more sober frame of mind and were drinking tea, perched on piles of assorted junk and making plans about their future.

'But before we do anything else,' said Susan matter-of-factly, 'we're going to deal with this lot. What we need is a plan.'

'I told you, I'll throw it all out for the sake of love,' he cried.

'Oh, don't start that again,' she laughed. 'No, there's things of value here—somewhere. It needs thought. Look, I tell you what, here's three good questions to ask about each thing you've got.'

She scribbled them down on a piece of paper and they really were good principles by which to deal with the excess of material clutter which most of us accumulate.

1. Is it of intrinsic personal value?
2. Do I use it?
3. Will I use it within the year?

'If it doesn't fit these categories, get rid of it,' she said firmly. 'Sell it, if possible, and give the money to the poor.'

He mused on what she had written for a few moments, then looked up brightly. 'Okay. I'll do it. I'll get some dustbin bags for the rubbish and we'll start tomorrow.'

Most believers do not have quite the same problem as the Courier. Or, at least, are not so untidy about it. Instead, they gradually accumulate possessions over the years. They fill lofts and cellars, drawers and cupboards. Vast sums are spent on sophisticated electronic entertainment, much of it produced by means of third-world economic slavery. Today more than ever before the average Englishman's home is his castle. No longer the open house but now the locked, burglar-proofed, visitor-proofed palace of sensual self-indulgence. And Christians must beware lest they succumb to the same sins.

The prophet Haggai revealed why in his day the people of God were frustrated and dissatisfied, in spite of their early vision for blessing. 'You have looked for much, and, lo, it came to little; and when you brought it home, I blew it away. Why? says the Lord of hosts. Because of my house that lies in ruins, while you busy yourselves each with his own house' (Haggai 1:9).

Satan actually brings disunity amongst God's people and hindrance to God's work by the simple strategem of distraction. Provided everyone is 'doing their own thing' and time, energy and money are tied up with homes, cars and hobbies, he has little to fear. On the other hand, when believers devote themselves to serving God, his church and his world, they have no time to be doped into materialistic apathy. Then they are a real threat to the kingdom of darkness. God's pilgrim church must learn to travel light if it is also to be an army on its toes. Get rid of the excess baggage. Ask of possessions, not only Susan's questions, but these:

Do I use it enough to justify keeping it?

Do I really need it?

Is it worth the time and money I spend on it?

Would it be of more use to someone else?

* * *

The sleek car hurtled around the winding mountain road, hugging each bend, mocking the gradients, exalting in power. Soaring Wagnerian music passionately proclaimed the dawn of a new age. Thunder crashed and lightning flashed. The stentorian voice of the commentator praised the performance of this magnificent machine. '0-60 in seven seconds, capable of 120 miles per hour, superb braking, the ultimate in luxury, a triumph of computer age technology and human genius, man and machine in mystic harmony, driving it is a spiritual experience!'

'Cor, dad! Can we get one?' cried Stephen. 'That's the sort of car I'd like.'

Mr Christian turned the television volume down while the commercials continued. 'Listen, son,' he said. 'Don't believe the adverts. Most people who buy that car are going to drive down ordinary roads and sit in ordinary traffic jams. Life just isn't like the commercials.'

'Yes, I know,' answered the young lad. 'But it's designed by computers. And it's got electronic ignition. And electric windows...and...and...'

'I know,' his father replied patiently. 'But it's still only a car.'

Stephen persisted. 'Yes, but it's better than ours. I mean, wouldn't you feel great driving one?'

'I'm sure I'd enjoy it very much. But listen, Stephen, owning things isn't the secret of happiness. I know the telly tries to tell you that but don't believe it. It's a lie.'

'Hm, s'pose so,' the lad agreed reluctantly. 'Hey, it's starting again. Can I turn the volume up?'

'Okay. But don't forget what I've said.'

Advertisers are continually trying to persuade us that life is enhanced by their products. We need to be critical of their claims but more especially of their emotional appeals, the music, the words, the images, which are all subtly designed to condition us into buying.

Some folk are exceedingly weak and go out to purchase what they see advertised the very next time they shop. Others are stronger but, nonetheless, have that gnawing hunger to buy things, because the hidden persuasion has conditioned their thinking. Believers must steadfastly resist the temptation. That can be done by developing spiritual discernment and by buying only in consultation with the Lord. But the best immunity is to be thoroughly committed and happy in a simple lifestyle.

Most children begin this way. When they are young they are so often wholly absorbed in something simple like a few twigs or a home-made game. But how quickly parents and grandparents spoil them with toys until their own creative instincts become atrophied under the welter of possessions. Christmas is the worst time. 'Train up a child in the way he should go, and when he is old he will not depart from it' is a double-edged proverb. Children reared on finding happiness in an ever constant supply of new toys and games will grow up to become bored materialists. Children taught appreciation and personal initiative will mature into happy, free adults. We cannot help but educate them in one way or the other.

Mr Christian went to answer the front door bell. The Courier and Susan stood on the doorstep looking very happy indeed. He invited them in and called his wife.

They were delighted to hear the good news of the couple's intended engagement and wished them God's blessing on their future together.

'There's something else we've done,' said Susan.

'What's that?' asked Mr Christian.

'We've cleared out Dai's room.'

'Hallelujah!'

'Yes, it took us three solid days' work. It was amazing. You just couldn't believe a room could hold so much.'

'How do you feel now, Dai?' Zoë asked.

'Oh, well, sort of clean, really. Uncluttered, you might say,' he replied with a laugh.

'Well, this is good news,' Mr Christian declared. 'You must be very happy indeed.'

The Courier's brow clouded slightly. 'We are, yes.' He hesitated. 'But there is one problem I'd like your advice on, if you don't mind.'

The other nodded encouragingly.

'It's...well...well, I've found quite a lot of bills, unpaid ones, you know, lying under all that rubbish.'

'Ah.'

'I don't want any money,' he spoke hastily lest he should be misunderstood. 'No, what I want to know is how I can handle my money properly in future 'cos I've never been much good at that, see. So can you give me some tips?'

Many people today are facing the Courier's problem and it is not unusual to find quite ordinary folk owing hundreds of pounds. Part of Christian wholeness is coming into a financial liberation that fulfils Paul's injunction, 'Owe no one anything' (Romans 13:8). This comes about by a combination of faith and responsible stewardship.

Mr Christian's first task was to ascertain what the Courier really owed. He pulled out a bundle of assorted bills. But further questioning revealed there were all sorts of other things as well. They made a list of the lot. This was followed by a list of his assets—which was not very encouraging.

Aside from a small amount of savings and his dole money, he had only the proceeds of what he had sold. It was not enough.

So they put the bills into an order of priority and he agreed to pay all he could at once and to write explanatory letters for the rest, promising to settle up as soon as possible.

'Not paying bills is really a form of stealing,' said Mr Christian. 'In future, you really must make it a priority to pay them as soon as they arrive. That's the only way to avoid the debt-trap. In fact, I think you should ask the Lord to bring you to the place where you could always pay your bills on demand if asked to do so.'

'In other words, don't spend what you haven't got. Is that what you mean?' Susan asked.

'More or less, yes. The fatal mistake so many make is to spend money from memory. And most of us tend to think we've got more than we actually have.'

The Courier possessed a bank account so they suggested he keep a running balance on his cheque book stubs of how much money he actually had left.

'Pay your bills. Deduct them from your balance. What's left is what you've got. Don't forget you need to save some for the next lot of bills, too—so put some aside and deduct that as well. The tiny bit left is all you can spend and you must never go over it!' was Mr Christian's simple advice.

'Can I ask you what you think about Christians using credit cards?' Susan enquired.

'They're all right if you use them *only* for the convenience of not carrying cash around. That means paying off the statement in full at the end of each month. If you can't do that, then don't have a credit card because it'll get you into debt. And the interest rates make them a very bad form of stewardship.'

The Courier pulled his card from his back pocket and offered it to Mr Christian.

'Here, take it will you. At least until I've cleared what I owe 'cos I'm not strong enough to live like that yet.'

Mr Christian said he would look after it but it was a purely voluntary thing and the Courier could have it back at any time. He was doing it only as a favour to help a friend.

They prayed together that the Lord would supply the Courier's needs and in particular that he would be able to find suitable employment in order to pay his way.

Three days later he jubilantly announced that he had got a job.

'The Lord's answered our prayers,' he cried. 'It's just the kind of thing I need. I'll be writing descriptive tourist guides for a publisher who specializes in that sort of thing.'

'That's marvellous, Dai,' Mr Christian responded, with equal delight.

'Those stern stone walls impassively overlooking the pageant of history...'

'Okay. We know,' Susan laughed. 'Promise we'll all buy it when it's published!'

'When do you start?' asked Mr Christian.

'Next Monday.'

'Terrific.'

*   *   *

The air was tense in Mr Aquarius' house. For two hours a heated debate had raged over the issue of the commune's finances. Most of the income came from yoga classes which Dawn conducted and lectures which her husband gave. The others donated part of their unemployment benefit. All were committed to not earning enough to pay tax so that they would not support the government's war machine.

However, bills were not being met, nor household chores being performed.

'Look, I think if you don't do anything else you could at least do some of the housework,' Dawn screeched at Tony who lolloped as usual in the corner.

'Hey! Cool it,' he drawled. 'I mean, like...cool it. I've got to meditate, you know. I'm still finding myself.'

'You're just a lazy slob!' she retorted angrily.

Tony was affronted. 'I see, that's how it is, is it? You talk about all this equality, all this sharing, this…community, but you don't really believe in it. Why isn't my *spiritual* contribution enough? Tell me that!'

Dawn turned to the others in exasperation. Karen was sitting in the lotus position quietly chanting. She had withdrawn. Mr Aquarius was at a loss.

'Well, I don't know the answer. But if we carry on at this rate the whole thing's going to fall apart. I mean, we've got to keep to the principles. We *did* say Tony could add his good vibrations to the community, didn't we?'

'I don't think his are good any more,' she replied.

'Hey, that's a value judgement,' he called. 'What's "good"? It's all relative. I think I bring peace to this pad. You're the one getting screwed up, sister. You've just gotta get cool, like me. That's my contribution.'

'But it won't pay the bills or get the work done,' Dawn growled between gritted teeth. 'Oh, I've had enough.'

And with that she stamped out of the room and slammed the door with a resounding crash. Mr Aquarius sighed.

'Perhaps that Mr Christian guy's right and it only works when you're born again,' Tony suggested sarcastically.

'Nonsense,' said Mr Aquarius.

CHAPTER TEN

Be Healed!

People today are much more health conscious than they were in previous generations. Improved public hygiene, better food, inoculations, free health care and decent housing have, for the first time in history, made it possible for the man in the street to experience good health. What was once the prerogative of the rich is now open to all—a triumph of human social achievement.

Yet this proud vision of the cure-all welfare state is waning in the eyes of many. The National Health Service is increasingly perceived as a dispirited bureaucratic juggernaut fast running out of fuel. People, waiting sometimes days for an appointment with their G.P. and months for a hospital consultation, are becoming disillusioned and even angry. Questions are being raised about both the quality and the kind of treatment being offered. Is it really a cure? Is this the best way? Why is it so impersonal, so time consuming?

Some feel we must take the matter into our own hands. Hence the proliferation of health clubs, magazines and television documentaries on everything from slimming to schizophrenia, biorhythms to brain surgery, aerobics to acne. Alternative self-help medicine is challenging both the assumptions and the monopoly of the professionals. Like it or not, it is here to stay. For the thousands who daily ply the doctors' surgeries with their ailments and the thousands more who just feel less than healthy, it offers a ray of hope.

'It seems to me that we've spent a lot of our time talking about alternative *preventive* medicine,' began the Courier. 'What I want to know is, what can we do for people when they actually get sick? I can see how important prevention is, but it's not the whole story now, is it?'

His question was not entirely objective because he had a cold coming on and was hoping for a quick cure from one of his companions, or at least some good advice.

'I also wish to know what the followers of the Lamb are seeing at this time,' added the Pilgrim Watcher with interest.

They were sitting in the Courier's room awaiting Mr Aquarius who had said he would be late. A vase of flowers, new curtains and a general sense of homely order evidenced that unique woman's touch upon their surroundings. Mr Christian was impressed with the difference Susan had made.

'I think I should just stress that our interest in prevention is related to our concern for wholeness. We don't want preventive medicine merely for its own sake, we want wholeness for Jesus' sake,' he replied. 'Following the path to true wholeness is the best preventive medicine I know, which leads in turn to better than average health.'

'Okay. I accept that. But even the best Christians get ill sometimes.' The Courier sneezed loudly. 'And the worst,' he added with a grin. 'So what are we to make of that? Are we supposed to accept illness? Or learn from it? Or what?'

'Well, let's be real about it,' Mr Christian answered. 'Most illness does no good at all. Nobody likes being sick and all of us treat it as an evil to be avoided. After all, that's why we try to get better. I'm not saying God doesn't bring good out of evil. The Bible says, "We know that in every-thing God works for good with those who love him, who are called according to his purpose" (Romans 8:28). But that doesn't mean physical suffering is a good thing.

'The reason I say that,' he explained, 'is because I don't think we should resign ourselves to the idea that sickness is just part of our lot in this life. I believe we should live expecting good health as a part of our wholeness. Even under the old covenant the people were told, "The Lord will take away from you all sickness; and none of the evil diseases of Egypt, which you knew, will he inflict upon you" (Deuteronomy 7:15). If obedience to the Law produced that kind of blessing we surely shouldn't expect less when we come to the obedience of faith. At the very least, our faith should give us substantial victory over the world's illnesses.

'Either because we are not entering into Christ's shalom, or as a result of doubts about our inheritance, we can so easily resign ourselves to sickness. It's unbelief which makes us vulnerable. Indeed, living in fearful expectation of a disease such as cancer can help bring it on.

'Some folk are especially exposed to this because they've been told, "It runs in the family",' continued Mr Christian. 'Faith must reply, "Yes, but does it run in God's family?" Paul wrote, "If any one is in Christ, he is a new creation; the old has passed away, behold, the new has come" (2 Corinthians 5:17). That doesn't mean we're freed from physical corruption—yet! But it does mean we're delivered from the fatalism of statistics. We're no longer subject to human chance, because we've come into the genetic inheritance of Christ, and diseases do not run in his family.'

Mr Christian went on to say that the full extent of this is yet to be realized. Part of the genetic make-up of Jesus is an inability to stay dead! That's why Paul could write, 'If the Spirit of him who raised Jesus from the dead dwells in you, he who raised Christ Jesus from the dead will give life to your mortal bodies also through his Spirit which dwells in you' (Romans 8:11). The day is coming when even that last enemy will be destroyed and all who die in Christ shall be gloriously raised from the dead to live for evermore in perfect health.

That is the goal. Meanwhile, faith enters in to that which is coming, to the fullest extent possible. We live and act with positive expectation. Even when things appear not to work out, and there are great mysteries in the sufferings and apparently untimely deaths of choice servants of God, then we worship and confess that 'to die is gain'. So Paul can write: 'This slight momentary affliction is preparing for us an eternal weight of glory beyond all comparison' (2 Corinthians 4:17). Faith will not be quenched; it always has grounds for making good confession.

'You know,' Mr Christian continued, 'Sometimes we invite illness just by what we say. Have you ever heard people talking like this? "It's going round." "Everybody's catching it." "I've got a cold coming." "I feel ill."

'What we really need is good confession and prayerful resistance at such times. My wife has taught me something about this—and you'll see the relevance, Dai. If ever she feels a cold coming, she'll go into a room alone and strongly rebuke it out loud. Since we've been doing this we've had far fewer colds and attacks of flu than we used to get.'

'Wish you'd told me that last night,' the Courier sniffed ruefully.

The Pilgrim Watcher was excited by this. 'So, you are beginning to realize that your fight is not with mere impersonal viruses? You talk to them! This is indeed progress.'

'Hang on,' said the Courier. 'Are you saying that viruses have intelligence—or are you saying they're actually demons? Cos that's a pretty mind-blowing concept.'

Mr Christian came in quickly. 'I don't think we humans can know precisely. There's some scientific evidence to suggest that viruses respond intelligently but whether that's demonic or not, I don't know. What we are sure of is that we're involved in a spiritual conflict and that Satan or his demons are at work behind every evil practice in this world.'

'You have spoken correctly,' agreed the Pilgrim Watcher. 'If you could see as I see, you would understand the abundance of spiritual activity, both good and evil, which is taking place all about you. This is not, as Mr Aquarius suggests, mere immaterial, neutral force. We Celestials have personalities—and so do the enemy.'

'We are not contending against flesh and blood, but against the principalities, against the powers, against the world rulers of this present darkness, against the spiritual hosts of wickedness in the heavenly places,' said Mr Christian, quoting from Ephesians 6:12.

The Courier wanted to know if all illness had a *direct* satanic cause.

Mr Christian replied, 'When we examine the Scriptures we find this is not the case. The book of Deuteronomy attributes a number of diseases including plague, ulcers, madness, blindness and dysentery to the direct hand of *God* against his foes. God's people were threatened with these diseases if they violated the covenant.

'Other illnesses result from sinful actions and attitudes. Over-indulgence in wine produces debility. Engaging with prostitutes leads to venereal disease. Rotten bones are caused by anger, and so on.

'However, the majority of illnesses, especially those dealt with by Jesus, are given no specific cause,' he continued. 'Their existence is taken as a matter of fact and we have to conclude that they are part of the futility of a fallen world. Things go wrong, accidents happen, because the creation is marred by sin.

'Now Satan takes full advantage of this fact and uses it to hold people in bondage. So, when Jesus came as the liberator, he tackled the most apparent areas of captivity, disease and demonization, and people knew the kingdom of God was coming into their midst. The early church was founded upon this basis. The followers of Jesus healed the sick, cast out demons and preached the good news at the same time declaring why this was happening and what men had to do about it. Before such an onslaught Satan's kingdom crumbled!'

Just then the bell rang and the Courier went to let Mr

Aquarius in. The latter was looking very pleased with himself. He flopped down into an armchair.

'Well, you're looking happy. What's the reason?' asked Mr Christian.

'We've just been able to heal somebody,' he answered with a smile. They pressed him to tell them what had happened.

'She's an old lady who came to me about two months ago complaining of indigestion and pains in her stomach as well as a feeling of weakness. She asked me if I could help.

'Well, we thought of changing her diet and tried that for a couple of weeks but it made no difference. So we decided to use pendulum diagnosis to find out where the trouble really was. She was very open to our approach so we laid her on a couch and prepared ourselves to receive guidance. I held the pendulum and, sure enough it began to oscillate violently over her abdomen. We opened ourselves further to the radiations and it clearly indicated that the problem was in her gall bladder. Dawn felt she had gall stones. As she said this the pendulum bucked violently. So we knew.'

Mr Christian had come across this approach to diagnosis. Radiesthesia is the broad term used to cover dowsing practices whether using a hazel fork, simple pendulum or some modern 'black box'. Psionic diagnosis is the particular technique used by Mr Aquarius. It claims to make use of the sensitivity to radiation which living creatures possess and skilled practitioners have not only successfully found water or diagnosed diseases but have been able to draw accurately otherwise hidden foundations of buildings by this method.

It is well recognized that mental blockages such as fear of the psychic will hinder its effectiveness as also will lack of faith in the instrument used, so a specially open mind is necessary for its success.

Divination of this or any other kind is roundly condemned in the Scriptures. 'There shall not be found among you any one...who practises divination.... For whoever does these things is an abomination to the Lord' (Deuteronomy 18:10–12). This passage does not define whether the powers are occult or human but clearly treats such practices as belonging to the enemy camp. Acts 16:16 describes a girl with 'a spirit of divination'. The word used, *puthon*, gives us the English, python. It refers to the demon-inspired cult of Apollo, the python-slayer.

Modern man may like to deny the existence of demons and in his pride he considers that an improvement in his psychic powers is a sign of evolutionary development. But in reality he is returning to ancient paganism and is consorting with dark powers. That apparently good results sometimes occur should hardly come as a surprise to those who know that Satan can disguise himself as an angel of light!

'Pray continue,' said the Pilgrim Watcher to Mr Aquarius. His voice was serious.

'Well, we put her on to a further course of healthy eating but we knew that wouldn't cure gall stones. So we've been holding a series of meditation sessions in order to reach out to her. We call it absent healing. Myself, I think it's much the same as when you Christians pray. We sought to communicate love and healing power to her and last night we really knew we were getting through. It was an incredible spiritual experience. And this morning she phoned to say the pain has completely gone. She's healed!'

'I'm glad she's better,' the Courier responded doubtfully. He glanced at the Pilgrim Watcher whose eyes flashed angrily.

'I know what took place last night,' he growled. 'In your vain desire to control destiny you called upon the gods. In your foolish ecstasy you called upon Roma, Krishna, Shiva, Buddha, Zoroaster, Mohammed *and Christ* and Isis and Venus. You brought my Lord Christ down to the level of those deceivers! You have blasphemed the Most High!'

His voice shook the room and fearsome power was revealed as he threw back his cloak and rose to his full height. What he had said was true and Mr Aquarius made no attempt to deny it. He trembled before the righteous glory of the Celestial and looked up at him beseechingly, a horrible realization threatening the barriers of his mind.

'But we intended good. Don't you recognize that? We just called on every good power we could think of. That's all.'

The Pilgrim Watcher was not impressed. The other two men shrunk back in their chairs expecting some bolt of lightning to destroy Mr Aquarius at any moment. But the bolt never fell. The anger seemed to fade and the atmosphere eased, as though the Pilgrim Watcher had been restrained by Another.

'You are commanded to repent,' he spoke sternly to Mr Aquarius. 'For you have committed iniquity and dwell in sin. There is but one Lord, even Jesus Christ. You will bow your knee to him.'

Mr Aquarius struggled to regain his composure but it was too much for him. His mind felt like a jumble of cogs and springs falling apart. He clutched his head in screaming confusion. Lights flashed before his eyes.

'It's not true. It can't be!' he cried. 'It's madness to believe. I will not. I must not.'

He stared wide-eyed first at the Pilgrim Watcher then at the Courier, then at Mr Christian. His breath came short and fast, sweat rolled down his face.

'You're mad! You're all mad!' he screeched in a delirium.

To his onlookers he appeared to be cracking-up. Mr Christian made to help him but before he could do so, with a demented cry of fear and fury mixed, Mr Aquarius fled the room.

They would have followed him but the Pilgrim Watcher bade them stay.

'The madness will pass, never fear. It may be then he will heed the voice of God. Pray that it be so.'

The two men nodded solemnly and sat emotionally drained themselves for some long while. At length the

Courier stirred himself.

'I'll put the kettle on and make us a cup of tea,' he said.

* * *

'I had a chap ring me up recently,' said Mr Christian. 'He was due to come and do some work but he said he'd got a sore throat. So I advised him to stay indoors and keep warm. I said it'd probably clear in a couple of days.

'You know, his reply amazed me. He's a believer and looks to me for spiritual counsel. Guess what he said? He'd go up to the doctor and he expected he'd be told to stay indoors for a couple of days! I couldn't believe it.'

'Ah, but there is the real question,' answered the Pilgrim Watcher knowingly.

It was about two hours after Mr Aquarius' abrupt departure and they were just finishing off some sandwiches, having partially recovered from the incident.

'What's the real question?' asked the Courier.

'Why, to what authority do you submit when you are not well,' the Celestial replied. 'What think you, Peter?'

'Hm. Yes. It depends what the real problem is, doesn't it?' Mr Christian pondered. 'As a rule I submit my car to the authority of a garage mechanic because he's best qualified to tackle its mechanical problems. At least, sometimes!

'Now if we think of our bodies and minds as just biochemical machinery then what we need is a scientist-technician to service them. And that's basically what modern doctors are trained to be, experts in repairing human machines!'

'But if we're more than that?...And we think we are...' interposed the Courier.

'Precisely. And if disease is more than just a physical breakdown then we need a different kind of expert,' Mr Christian said. 'See, we're agreed that all illnesses have their origin either in the fall, or in Satan's wiles or in some specific sin. That means they're spiritual at root and need a spiritual remedy.'

'Which means the sick person needs to seek out a spiritual expert,' concluded the Courier.

'There is, in the New Testament, but one clear command to those who are sick,' declared the Pilgrim Watcher. 'It is written by James. "Is any among you sick? Let him call for the elders of the church; and let them pray over him, anointing him with oil in the name of the Lord" ' (James 5:14).

Mr Christian nodded. 'I take it to mean ill enough to need a doctor or chemist. But, yes, that's quite consistent with other biblical teaching which says shepherds are to be healers. God's criticism of the shepherds in Ezekiel 34 was that they had failed to do this.'

He picked up a Bible and read: 'The weak you have not strengthened, the sick you have not healed, the crippled you have not bound up...' (Ezekiel 34:4).

'Every pastor is to be a doctor,' murmured the Courier. 'A radical thought!'

'Yes, and a psychiatrist,' added Mr Christian. 'That word only means someone who treats the soul, after all. Modern psychiatrists are really secular pastors.'

He continued: 'There's need for a radical approach. The church, by and large, has abandoned its healing role in both the realms of mind and body, trying to somehow isolate the "spirit" from the rest and concentrate on that. But life doesn't work so neatly. People are complex structures and we have to treat the whole man.'

He said the fruit of this abandonment has been a redefining of man in purely secular, materialistic terms and treatment is given based on that redefinition. Spectacular as some of the successes have been, we must not be blinded by the fundamentally false assumptions of modern medicine. As we note the challenge which those like Mr Aquarius are making, we must rediscover the power of divine healing in the church based upon scriptural principles concerning the nature of man and disease.

'Pastors need training in the ministry of healing,' Mr Christian went on. 'It must be seen as a legitimate and necessary part of eldership. Men in leadership must take God's word seriously on this. But the people, too, need to change. We're conditioned to rushing to the doctors or the chemists at the first sign of illness. That is a worldly conditioning. Our minds need renewing if we are to bring faith to bear upon our ailments.'

'Does this mean doctors are obsolete?' asked the Courier.

'No, I don't think so,' Mr Christian answered. 'If I understand it aright, what James is saying is that all illness is a spiritual issue and must first be submitted to *spiritual* authority. That is channelled through the elders. It means we look to God for healing, not to men. James goes on to say, "The prayer of faith will save the sick man, and the Lord will raise him up; and if he has committed sins, he will be forgiven" (James 5:15).

'I don't think that means we can't use medicine,' he added. 'But it needs to be a spiritual decision taken before God, in consultation with the elders. Very often medication will be unnecessary, but sometimes God will direct that way.

'We get into impossible inconsistencies if we say we don't ever believe in using human agencies. It would mean if a child were to break his arm in the park, for example, we'd do nothing to help except pray. Even loosening his clothes to treat him for shock would be wrong. To put a plaster on a cut, or even to wash it for that matter, would be an act of blatant unbelief!

'God has built goodness into his creation. The doctrine of providence teaches us that he is at work in all good agencies for the general blessing of mankind,' Mr Christian explained. 'It's what Jesus meant when he said that the Father "Makes his sun to rise on the evil and on the good, and sends rain on the just and on the unjust" (Matthew 5:45). He has also given mankind a creation mandate to subdue the earth. Of course, he wants us to do that in dependence upon him.

'And there's the rub for modern man. We've developed medical science autonomously. What we so desperately need today are God-dependent doctors working in harmony with spiritual leaders, knowing when to use medicine in faith and when to use the word of healing in faith.'

The following passage from an old Jewish writing conveys something of a godly balance on the issue.

> Honour a physician according to your need of him with the honour due to him: for truly the Lord has created him. For from the Most High comes healing; and from the king he shall receive a gift. The skill of the physician shall be admired. The Lord created medicines out of the earth: and a prudent man will have no disgust at them. Was not water made sweet with wood, that the virtue of it might be known? And he gave men skill, that he might be glorified in his marvellous works. With them he heals and takes away his pain. With these the chemist will make a medicine; and his work shall not be brought to an end; and from him is peace upon the face of the earth.
>
> My son, in your sickness do not be negligent; but pray to the Lord and he shall heal you. Put away wrong doing, and order your hand aright, and cleanse your heart from all manner of sin. Give a sweet savour and a memorial of fine flour; and make your offering fat, as one that is not. Then give place to the physician, for truly the Lord has created him; and do not let him go from you, for you have need of him. There is a time when in their very hands is the issue for good. For they also shall beseech the Lord, that he may prosper them in giving relief and in healing for the maintenance of life. He that sins before his Maker, let him fall into the hands of the physician. (Ecclesiasticus 38:1–15 RV modernized)

Mr Christian said, 'The ancient Jews viewed all of life as sacred. Part of our modern predicament is that we've put things like faith and medicine into different compartments and created a two-tier world.'

'What do you mean?' asked the Courier.

Mr Christian asked for a sheet of paper and wrote out the following:

SPIRITUAL—Faith, forgiveness, prayer, holiness, etc
MATERIAL—Medicine, science, economics, education, etc

He explained: 'This is how secular man thinks—and sometimes Christians too. But a proper understanding of the kingdom of God means bringing spiritual values to bear on the issues of life. This is the only way to avoid inconsistency, confusion and condemnation when we approach healing.'

He drew another diagram thus:

THE KINGDOM OF GOD

Faith, forgiveness, prayer, holiness, etc

Medicine, science, economics, education, etc

'All right,' said the Courier. 'So we accept that we can go to doctors sometimes and that can still be an expression of faith. But what sort of doctors? And what kind of medicine is acceptable? If we can use conventional medicine why not at least some holistic medicine?'

'Part of the difficulty in answering those questions is simply knowing where to draw the line between conventional and unorthodox medicine,' Mr Christian replied. 'For example, drug companies buy up phenomenal quantities of herbs and other plants from which they distil and purify the particular part they want. That's called conventional. But if a local herbalist brews up the same plant as a herb tea and prescribes smaller quantities over a longer period, that's dubbed unorthodox.'

'Like, when does physiotherapy turn into holistic massage?' the Courier said.

'That's right,' said Mr Christian. 'It's difficult to know where one ends and the other begins. You see, today's unorthodox treatment might be recognized tomorrow as a medical breakthrough. Although scientifically trained doctors would like to go from one verified step of research to another, quite often new treatments come, as it were, out of the blue, and it's only later that we realize how they work.

'I remember reading of a man with a chronic leg ulcer which wasn't responding to conventional treatment,' he recalled. 'Then someone recommended covering it with crushed papaya fruit. Lo and behold it worked! Now that sounded thoroughly "alternative". That is, until it was realized that papaya contains an enzyme called papain which digests proteins. The idea of an enzyme eating up the putrifying matter so that the ulcer could heal actually makes good scientific sense. Now if papain comes to be used as a standard treatment, it ceases to be "alternative".'

The Courier nodded. 'So it may be that quite a lot of holistic healing will be shown to have a scientific basis?'

'Yes,' said Mr Christian. 'But you must remember that definitions of science are changing and many practices may well fit into a broader understanding of science which includes parapsychology, extra sensory perception and the like.'

'The Materialistic-Magician again,' proffered the Pilgrim Watcher.

'Precisely,' replied Mr Christian. 'And that's the point where some so-called unorthodox treatments become unacceptable to us because we believe that their effectiveness depends upon evil spiritual forces, and they require us to embrace a world-view which is contrary to the Scriptures.'

'So we need to choose our doctors and our remedy with great care, if we feel it right to use such means at all?' asked the Courier.

'Yes, we must discern spirits at all times,' his friend replied. 'Perhaps I could give an example of what I mean. Let's talk about homeopathy.'

For the benefit of his companions Mr Christian explained that homeopathy was first proposed as a coherent medical doctrine by Hahnemann in 1755. He demonstrated that a very diluted dose of a substance which produces a set of symptoms in a healthy person could be used to treat disorders manifesting similar symptoms in a sick person. Making an accurate assessment of both the general and local symptoms displayed by his patients he prescribed medicine which paralleled those symptoms; like was treated by like.

Today's proponents stress that homeopathic treatment has the advantage of inducing recovery by stimulating the body to fight the disease. For example, a small amount of an allergen may desensitize the patient to a known allergy by stirring up the body's own resistance. This is really an extension of the principle behind vaccination, inoculation and immunization.

Homeopathic treatment aims to treat the whole person and effect a complete cure rather than simply attacking a particular disease. Toxic side-effects from powerful drugs are avoided which makes treatment particularly safe for children.

It is in the realm of indefinable conditions such as allergies, asthma and migraine that homeopathy has been particularly effective.

'I can see nothing inherently wrong with homeopathy, at least not spiritually,' said Mr Christian. 'But neither do I see it as being necessarily better than orthodox medicine. It is certainly not more spiritual. We need faith in God for healing, not in some remedy which claims to be more natural.

'However, I must make one big qualification,' he added. 'Not all homeopathic and herbal remedies are so spiritually neutral. You may easily come across practitioners today who are into Mr Aquarius' New Age Consciousness and are dabbling with all kinds of dubious treatments. These people may well believe that their medicines contain mystic properties or essential forces. I would strongly advise anyone to steer well clear of those, even if they claim to be Christian. You *must* be sure of the authority to which you submit yourself.'

'Hmm. It's that question of authority again,' said the Courier. 'One more question. What do I do about my cold?'

Mr Christian laughed. 'I guess everyone's got their own patent remedy. For what it's worth, I'll tell you what mine is. If I haven't managed to stop it coming and I know I've got a cold, I seek the Lord and ask him to heal me quickly. Then I take a very large dose of vitamin C powder, say two grams. Add to this a cup of hot sweet milk laced with rum and an aspirin and go to bed. You'll sleep like a log and sweat like a pig but'll probably be over the worst by morning! Try it if you like but I'm taking no responsibility for the results; you seek the Lord for yourself.'

'I wonder where Susan's put the rum,' murmured the Courier. 'Well, if you don't mind, gentlemen, I think I will take to my bed 'cos I am feeling rather rough, see.'

His companions took their cue to leave.

*   *   *

Susan was in absolute agony. She blinked back the tears as another bolt of pain seared through her back. It had come on quite suddenly in the middle of the afternoon and slowly intensified as the day wore on. By early evening she could not move without the steady ache turning into sharp stabbing pain.

Of course, she had prayed, but nothing had happened. She thought about the bottle of pain killers in the cupboard, left over from her previous treatment.

'No, I'm not going to take them,' she gasped through gritted teeth. She resolved to catch a bus and go over to Mr and Mrs Christian. 'Lord, just give me strength and ease the pain enough for me to get there,' she prayed earnestly.

Half an hour later Mrs Christian opened the front door to find Susan pale and trembling before her.

'Why, Susan, dear, what's wrong?' cried Zoë.

Susan fell into her arms and burst into tears. 'It's my back. The pain's come back but worse than ever before,' she sobbed.

Zoë called her husband and together they gently lowered her on to a hard chair.

'Why has it started up again?' Susan asked plaintively. 'I really thought the Lord would keep me well from now on. And things have been going so good, what with Dai and everything.'

'I think you're under a satanic attack,' said Mr Christian quietly. 'And I suspect there's some kind of vulnerability left from when you were with the commune. Look, we've not asked you this before, but what kind of treatment did Karen give you when you first went to her?'

Susan explained that she had submitted to a combination of acupuncture and acupressure.

Acupuncturists claim that the technique was practised in China at least 2,500 years before Christ. Years of observation have defined some 800 acupuncture points which all follow a definite pattern over the body. Imaginary lines link various series of points associated with particular organs. These lines are called meridians and twelve are of particular importance.

Inserting needles at specific acupuncture points along the appropriate meridian is said to stimulate the nerves to send electrical impulses to the spinal cord and lower brain and thus on to the diseased area. These impulses may stimulate the organ to function better or cause it to reduce its operation, as required. Different needles achieve different effects, for example, silver is a sedative and gold a stimulant.

As the twelve main meridians are said to be reflected in the radial artery, the selection of the appropriate meridian is done by pulse diagnosis. A skilled practitioner claims that by feeling the patient's pulse he can detect not only past and present illnesses but anticipate what is coming—in which case acupuncture can be used as a preventive therapy. It is not a cure-all treatment but claims have been made for its success over migraine, arthritis, sciatica, psoriasis, anxiety, depression, asthma, bronchitis and ulcers. It is also used as an anaesthetic.

Variations include putting minute electrical charges on the needles and using acupressure which is a needle-less stimulation of the acupuncture points.

No clear evidence has been found to suggest that such nerve-organ connections physically exist. The philosophy behind acupuncture is Taoism and the meridian lines are considered to be psychic energy pathways along which this energy, or ch'i, flows to the different organs. All illness is due to an imbalance of yin and yang, negative and positive, the complementary opposites which constitute this Universal Life Force. Stimulation of the acupuncture points sets out to restore the balance and thereby improve health.

As has been shown, the existence of the life force is a deception based upon an impersonal view of the universe. The effectiveness of acupuncture depends upon more than a little parapsychology or, as a Christian would put it, acupuncture draws upon the power of elemental spirits. As such, it must be unacceptable to believers. Whether secular research will ever show it to have a solid physical basis is an open question but the fact remains that the vast majority of practitioners are generally committed to a false doctrine of reality. Submission to such techniques exposes us to the possibility of demonic assault.

Mr Christian addressed Susan, 'I've more than a feeling that you are being attacked by a vengeful spirit because of your exposure to all this.' He explained what had transpired between the men earlier that day. 'All the time there was hope of some alliance, things were quiet, but that possibility ceased this afternoon. This is a kick-back.'

'Well, what shall I do?' cried Susan in desperation. 'I don't want any part of that business any more. I really want to be separated to the Lord.'

'You need to renounce utterly your involvement with these practices, Susan,' answered Zoë. 'I think we should minister some deliverance and healing, don't you, Peter?'

Her husband agreed. They explained what they would do and began to pray in tongues.

'Lord, I really do hate the devil,' Susan declared earnestly. 'I want you alone to be Lord. I'm truly sorry for ever going from you, you know that. Now please set me free from everything evil which came from that time. I renounce the lot, in Jesus' name. Amen.'

Mr Christian prayed, 'Father, we believe in the authority of Jesus over every other power in this universe. We confess him to be the conqueror of Satan and Lord of all. Hallelujah! Praise you for the power of your Holy Spirit sent upon us to heal and deliver in Jesus' name. We call upon you, for your glory's sake, to set Susan free. We sever her from all her past involvements; we break the power, in Jesus' all-powerful name!

'You vengeful spirit, we command you, in the name of God's appointed Judge to loose your hold from Susan's body. All who gained access during her backsliding we command you to depart in the name of Jesus!'

A jolt of pain hit Susan like a sledgehammer. She cried out, then coughed violently.

'Dear Father,' Zoë prayed. 'Now heal and restore your dear child to full health and strength. Put right everything that has been damaged and make her completely whole. Let your healing Spirit touch her now.'

Susan went weak at the knees and was gently lowered to the floor. She lay peacefully in the presence of God. At length she opened her eyes and smiled serenely.

'It's gone,' she spoke in a relieved voice. 'It's gone!'

They helped her up and asked her to move about. There was no pain and no stiffness. The Lord had healed her.

Together they praised God for his love and grace.

'Phew! I feel exhausted,' exclaimed Susan.

'I'm not surprised,' replied Zoë with a laugh. 'Come on, give me a hand to make a cuppa while she rests will you, Peter?'

Susan's healing was, in many ways, a straightforward case. Not all ailments are so simple nor so overtly satanic in origin and dilemmas remain for many of God's people, especially those who suffer chronic diseases in spite of having put everything right, trusted God and received ministry. It is no answer to say they lack faith when clearly they don't. We must take into account other factors concerning the overall expectation of the church, the times and seasons of God's will and the opposition of Satan.

At present, many are feeling the stirrings of the Spirit on the matter of signs and wonders, and in particular, of healings. There needs to be faith for the fulfilment of that growing expectation. Satan will oppose it; if he can, he will have believers retreat from the challenge and rationalize away what the Bible says. That would be a major victory for him. Christians must persevere and not be discouraged when things appear not to work out. God is the God of the breakthrough and the church stands on the brink of one of those tremendous moves of the Spirit which through the centuries have from time to time swept over the nations.

A release of healing power is about to speak volumes to a worried world and open the ears of mankind to the rest of the gospel as never before in this generation. Already first fruits are coming; the harvest ripens. 'For still the vision awaits its time; it hastens to the end—it will not lie. If it seem slow, wait for it; it will surely come, it will not delay' (Habakkuk 2:3).

CHAPTER ELEVEN

Fighting Fit

Thousands jogging the streets and parks of London. Hundreds more doing their daily aerobics. Health food shops springing up like mushrooms. New-fangled techniques for relaxing. Exotic cures for anything from corns to cancer. The search for meaning through mystic exploration.

'But what's it all for? What's the point of this pursuit of health?' the Courier pondered as he lay upon his bed. 'Sure, it's better than being breathless, weak and constipated, let alone neurotic, depressed and confused. But in the end, in the final analysis, what purpose does it all serve?'

He reached to the bedside cabinet and fumbled for his Bible. His thoughts led him to the Book of Ecclesiastes and he turned the pages, picking out verses here and there. 'What does man gain by all the toil at which he toils under the sun?...I have seen everything that is done under the sun; and behold, all is vanity and a striving after wind...For who knows what is good for man while he lives the few days of his vain life, which he passes like a shadow?...For man has no good thing under the sun but to eat, and drink, and enjoy himself...' (Ecclesiastes 1:3,14; 6:12; 8:15).

'That's it for the unbeliever, surely,' he declared aloud. 'The best hope he has is for a reasonably happy life while it lasts—life, liberty and the pursuit of happiness. But I want more than that.'

He swung himself out of bed. 'I must talk to Peter about this,' he decided.

The two men met later that morning for a game of badminton at the Crook Log Sports Centre, Bexleyheath. Neither was particularly good but they thoroughly enjoyed themselves on the pleasant court. Afterwards, as they sat in the bar overlooking the badminton hall, the Courier raised the matter on his mind.

'It's all futile!' he blurted out.

Mr Christian was startled and the Courier grinned at his reaction.

'Oh, not me being a Christian or anything like that, in case you're worried,' he hastily reassured his friend. 'No, I mean this secular health trip. It doesn't lead anywhere. I mean, it's nice to be fit and good-looking, I suppose, but, in the end, what's it for? It's just vanity.'

His eyes followed an attractive, shapely girl across to the bar. Then he remembered Susan and felt guilty. He looked away quickly. Mr Christian smiled and nodded towards the girl.

'She's doing all right on it, though, isn't she? Young, fit, confident, curving in all the right places.'

The Courier blushed slightly. 'Come on, you know what I mean. What's she living for?'

'Why don't you ask her?' suggested his companion with a grin.

The Courier looked doubtfully at the girl, then at Mr Christian. Only then did it dawn on him that his leg was being pulled. He gave a relieved laugh.

'Listen, Dai, if she enjoys playing sport and feels better for it, surely that's a good thing? After all, it makes sense to do something about our health rather than just hope we'll survive our allotted span without too many troubles.'

'That's what Ecclesiastes more or less implies, I suppose,' the Courier answered. 'But it still says life's futile, for all that.'

'And so it is. But better to be healthily futile than unhealthily so, don't you agree?'

'Whose side are you on today?'

'Oh, the usual one,' Mr Christian replied goodnaturedly. 'It's just that we mustn't knock those who aren't Christians too hard for their efforts in the right direction, just because they don't see ultimate reality. Most people take life as it comes and try to make the best of it. It takes real revelation from God to see the futility and to recognize that even the most successful are wasting their existence.

'I think what we have to ask ourselves is whether *we* aren't in danger of pursuing wholeness simply because of the world's current craze for it. If so, we'll be sharing in their—albeit healthy—futility and nothing more.'

'I suppose that's what's concerning me underneath,' the Courier replied.

'Well, do you remember shortly after we first met, we spoke about *shalom*, that biblical word for wholeness? God had the idea long before we cottoned on to it. So we're not responding to a futile fad but to the will of God.

Mr Christian continued, 'The truth is, if we believers had really been living in wholeness and spreading the message properly, we wouldn't be in the mess we are today. And Leo wouldn't have a hearing for his deceptive ideas.'

'Okay. So you're reminding me it's the will of God, and I see that. But does he just want me to be whole as an end in itself? Because I'd still feel that was a bit vain,' responded the Courier.

Mr Christian reminded him of Paul's words to the Colossians about Christ: 'For in him all the fullness of God was pleased to dwell, and through him to reconcile to himself all things, whether on earth or in heaven, making peace by the blood of his cross' (Colossians 1:19–20).

'God has established the model and the source of wholeness in his Son; his purpose is for that wholeness to be reproduced in others and ultimately for it to be restored to the entire universe. Yet, to achieve that end, it was necessary for Jesus to lay down his life.

'That's the key to grasping the significance of our own wholeness,' Mr Christian enthused. 'It's for others and for the realization of God's eternal purpose. He isn't much interested in seeing us solve all our psychological hang-ups, eating the right food, living a balanced lifestyle and all the rest of it, just so that we can enjoy a comfortable life surrounded by mutually admiring friends. No, we exist for his sake, and that means laying down our wholesome life for others.'

' "By this we know love, that he laid down his life for us; and we ought to lay down our lives for the brethren," ' the Courier quoted 1 John 3:16 from memory.

'Yes, you might also describe the truly whole person as one who has been perfected in love. And the nature of God's love is that it always wants to give,' his companion replied. 'The thing is, we can only give what we've got. If our lives lack the shalom of God we'll not be able to do much for anyone else.

'I knew a chap once, as orthodox a preacher as they come, steeped in Reformed theology. With the truth he knew he should've packed his church; but he emptied it instead. In fact, it closed down. D'you know why? Because he lacked wholeness in his own life. So he'd, say, preach on the peace of God but actually minister tension. He'd share on God's love but it'd come out as a threat. He believed in the victory of Christ but finished his course by delivering a series on Satan that was so depressing that the remaining few members of his congregation gave up.'

The Courier grimaced.

'Ever since the Word became flesh, God has always "fleshed" the Word; doctrine is enshrined in people, not simply in the head, but in the whole person.' Mr Christian was earnest. 'All these fractured lives around us will be healed when they receive the Word of God expressed through renewed people. The reconciliation of all things can only occur as the body of Christ experiences the fullness of the Head and sacrificially shares that with a needy world.

This is a challenge to wholeness which preserves us from the futility of self-centredness.'

'We must be going,' said the Courier glancing at the time. 'The Pilgrim Watcher has asked us to meet him on Blackheath this afternoon. I think it may be his farewell. I'm bringing Susan. Can Zoë be there as well?'

The other nodded and with that they departed for lunch.

*   *   *

Though the weather was still warm, moderate cloud was building up as they assembled on that historic heath overlooking the south bank of the Thames. The Courier gave the sky a doubtful glance. It might rain soon.

'Welcome,' cried the Pilgrim Watcher. 'My time is almost complete, and I have but one more matter to discuss with you ere I depart. Won't you please be seated?'

They arranged themselves on the grass as the Pilgrim Watcher readied himself to write. He addressed them again.

'I have seen much that evidences the need for the Lamb's wholeness in this society. Encouraged I have been too, that you are not silent upon the subject. (Here, he addressed Mr Christian in particular.) That Dai and Susan have found the Way causes me profound rejoicing. Yet Mr Aquarius presents a serious challenge, a seductive alternative to the way of Christ, one which all but ensnared you, Susan. My question is this: how ready is the church to meet this need and this challenge?'

It was Susan who spoke first.

'The church I used to attend isn't at all,' she said. 'I don't think they even know what's going on. I could see no evidence of the Holy Spirit there. If there had been I don't think I would have left in the first place.'

'But things are changing in all sorts of unlikely places,' Zoë insisted. 'So nowhere is hope entirely absent—at least, not yet.'

'I think it's in those churches where the Spirit has been

given liberty to move that the answer to your question lies,'
Mr Christian addressed the Pilgrim Watcher.

The Courier agreed, though admitted his experience was
rather limited.

Between them, Mr and Mrs Christian explained a little
of what had been happening in many churches over the
preceding years. They began with the first of the con-
temporary movings of the Spirit which took place in the
early 1960s at a time when the church was being all but
swamped by the tidal wave of what was to be hailed as a
second renaissance. Subsequent history has amply demonstrated that that renaissance was but the angel of death in
psychedelic clothing. The swinging sixties led to the
searching seventies, and thence to the empty eighties.

But the moving of the Spirit was genuine and has continued apace ever since. What began with a few people
being baptized in the Spirit has now radically affected
whole churches. Tentative back-room experiences have
become congregational norms. Truths long buried under
the dusty weight of tradition, ignorance and fear are now
eagerly embraced by tens of thousands. There is no doubt
that a breath of fresh life is blowing through many churches.

'There have been decisive landmarks in this work of
God,' Mr Christian observed. 'In the first place, churches
had to decide whether to receive baptism in the Spirit as a
valid and necessary experience. Later on, the issue was
whether to return to the pattern of the New Testament
church life or to restrict the Spirit within the old framework
of sub-biblical tradition.'

'And today?' queried the Courier.

'The challenge to churches who have come this far is to
take on the great social and moral issues of the hour, to
engage in spiritual warfare and Spirit-anointed evangelism.
The alternative is to live out their remaining years as
self-contented holy huddles,' he replied.

'It seems to me that there are two dangers,' Zoë commented. 'There are churches which are attempting to reach

the world but without renewing themselves. They see the need outside but are blind to the real nature of their own need. Their evangelism is always going to be like trying to fill a sieve! Then there are those restored churches which could so easily become introverted and smug because they've got so much that's good. God forbid that we should eke out our days in halo-polishing!' she said firmly.

'But be fair, dear,' her husband responded. 'The voice of the prophets *is* being heard and we've been around long enough to see the extent to which many churches have been restored to New Testament wholeness. I agree there are dangers of falling short—the better is often the enemy of the best—but I've confidence that God is at work and nothing is going to stop him from fulfilling his entire purpose.'

The Pilgrim Watcher desired to know what they saw as the distinctive marks of churches which are keeping abreast of the Spirit's moving. He waited quietly while the others briefly discussed their answer. They came up with five particular features.

'The first is to do with the nature of church membership,' said Mr Christian. 'Many traditional churches are little more than religious clubs. The members pay their dues, attend the functions and vote on various issues but retain their private lives outside. In fact, some may not even be truly born again. That's not New Testament wholeness.'

'Ephesians 1:23 describes the church as "his body, the fullness of him who fills all in all". It's a living, organic thing rather than a mere organization. So, to be a real member it's essential to be born again and be baptized in the Spirit. That must be the actual experience of the whole membership, not just an ideal.'

'We talk a lot about commitment,' Zoë explained. 'That's because we want people to be really grafted into the life of Christ and not just, as it were, tied on with a bit of string. As far as possible, we try to make sure that folk really are born again and have expressed repentance and faith.'

'Yes, that's the ground upon which we baptize them and

pray for them to be baptized in the Spirit,' her husband added. 'That's the biblical way of being received into the church. It's a deep total life commitment.'

'So we live very much as a community,' Zoë continued. 'There's a sense of fellowship, care and sharing which goes far beyond meetings. Our lives relate at every level. It's really like being in a big family of love. In fact, in our experience it's the coming into that kind of environment which is one of the biggest factors in making people whole.'

'A reconciling body,' murmured the Courier.

'The second distinctive feature is the nature of our leadership,' Mr Christian continued. 'Traditional churches either seem to be run by a professional elite clergy of some kind or they employ a man to do pastoral work subject to the democratic wishes of the membership. Neither approach is scriptural. The New Testament teaches the priesthood of all believers and that abolishes the idea of a special class of professional priests. And democracy is a secular concept not a biblical one, anyway.'

'So how have you resolved that?' Susan queried.

He replied that the key is to be found in Ephesians 4:7–16 where Paul teaches that the ascended Christ has appointed five types of word-ministry—apostles, prophets, evangelists, pastors and teachers—in order to equip the body to function and mature. A proper understanding of divine appointing and anointing enables a church to recognize God-given ministries and to submit to their teaching. Neglect of any one of these gifts will leave a fellowship sorely lacking.

'This issue of authority is an important one today,' commented the Courier. 'How do you avoid the danger of authoritarianism? I can see professional priests might be like that but there are at least institutional safeguards.'

'It's a good point,' Mr Christian replied. 'I believe the answer lies in first of all recognizing that the nature of spiritual leadership is different from the world's.'

He quoted the words of Jesus: ' "You know that the rulers of the Gentiles lord it over them, and their great men exercise authority over them. It shall not be so among you: but whoever would be great among you must be your servant, and whoever would be first among you must be your slave; even as the Son of man came not to be served but to serve, and to give his life a ransom for many" (Matthew 20:25–28).

'God-appointed leaders seek to serve the people, not to build their own empires,' he explained. 'That doesn't mean they're to be "ever so 'umble" like Uriah Heep. The servant of the Lord has tremendous authority behind him, but it's the Lord's, not his own.'

'The other safeguard surely lies in relationships,' Zoë came in. 'Our leaders share their lives together in open honest friendship. They look after each other. Even apostles exercise mutual submission—so there's no pyramid of power with Mr X at the top.

'To know that the leaders over me submit to one another gives me great security,' she added.

'Yes, submitting to one another in the fear of the Lord is a primary outcome of being filled with the Spirit,' concluded her husband, referring to Ephesians 5:18–21.

The Courier had been impressed from the beginning by the worship at Mr Christian's church. He wanted to know why it was so different from traditional worship.

'It's all to do with an understanding of David's tabernacle,' Mr Christian replied enigmatically, with a twinkle in his eye.

The Courier gave him one of those 'that's a fat lot of help' looks.

'Okay. Explain it to the novice, will you?'

In Acts 15:16, James the leading elder of the Jerusalem church, summing up the debate over the inclusion of the Gentiles, quotes the words of the prophet Amos, which, he says, are being fulfilled in the new covenant: "After these things I will return, and I will rebuild the Tabernacle of David which has fallen, and I will rebuild its ruins, and I will restore it" (NASB).

Mr Christian explained how David had erected a tent in Jerusalem to house the ark of God which contained the stone tablets of the Law and how he appointed an order of worship which anticipated the new covenant. Whereas the tabernacle of Moses spelt out separation from God, the tabernacle of David declared the reality of God's presence in the midst of his people. It foreshadowed the access to the Lord's presence which is such a feature of the new covenant. The proper response to this was continual exuberant praise. It is interesting to note that almost all the psalms were composed at this time.

'I consider much of traditional church worship to be a christianized tabernacle of Moses approach to God,' he said, 'It's building-centred, formal, ceremonial and solemn—essentially suited to those living under Law.

'What's taking place today is a rediscovery of the significance of the tabernacle of David for worship. We're also learning about its implications for the new order of priesthood which New Testament believers enter.

'The New Testament commands us to sing the psalms, as well as other songs, in our worship and we also put them into practical expression. As a friend of mine says: "How can we sing the psalms yet not do what they say?" What you see in our meetings is the Holy Spirit inspiring praise suited to a tabernacle where every believer can come as close to God as the minister himself.

'So, the way we worship is the third feature of our church today,' concluded Mr Christian.

'Then it's not just the bright idea of a few extroverts but obedience to the Scriptures?' nodded the Courier. 'I like it, too—well, David's my namesake now, isn't he?' He held out his hands appealingly to Susan who laughed and agreed.

One of the major causes of superficiality in the church at large is the lack of adequate discipling of the members and this was the fourth distinctive feature to which Mr Christian drew their attention.

'It's really related to the whole nature of membership,

which was our first point,' he explained. 'Club-type membership is almost always superficial—no one expects a person to do much more than keep the rules and be generally supportive of the cause. But family membership involves our total lifestyle and that means being open to change in every area of our lives.

'There's a clear mandate in Scripture for mutual discipling. Jesus said we were to go and make, not just converts, but disciples of all nations. A disciple is one who has not only learned truths from his master but also lives them. He submits, not only his head, but his whole life to the teacher.

'The Lord uses his body the church to facilitate this process. Paul instructs the Colossians, "Let the word of Christ dwell in you richly, as you teach and admonish one another in all wisdom..." (Colossians 3:16). The word translated "admonish" has the idea of dynamically confronting someone with the truth, with a view to a change of mind leading to a change of conduct. That's the essence of discipling.'

Zoë explained, 'In our church we do this all the time in the course of our relationships but we also meet in small groups for that specific purpose. Obviously, everyone who comes to us submits to this process willingly. We're not talking about brainwashing or browbeating but a responsible, loving opening of our lives to one another and to the word of God. I believe it's one of the most vital factors in my own spiritual growth towards wholeness,' she acknowledged.

'Yes, there's no better means of making us doers of the word and not just hearers,' endorsed her husband.

'I can see this restoration of wholeness to the church will attract many seekers,' observed the Pilgrim Watcher, resting his quill for a moment. 'But the lost also need finding. I take it your last feature is concerned with that.'

They nodded.

'In one sense the whole thing is a reaching out to the lost,' said Mr Christian. 'Jesus told us to be a city set on a hill whose light could not be hidden. I believe what is being produced today is shining as a ray of hope to those who have despaired of traditional religion as well as empty secularism. But, you're quite right, we're increasingly involved in actively reaching the lost.'

'So you're doing evangelism?' asked Susan.

'I don't really like the word,' he replied. 'It's got connotations of an activity tagged on to church life, usually for short periods of time. Being witnesses for Jesus and establishing the kingdom of God amongst the unbelievers is a way of life, not an optional extra, as I understand it.

'What we're seeing today is the beginning of a rediscovery of the New Testament apostolic and evangelistic thrust that turned the world upside down,' he said.

He explained how the early disciples proclaimed the good news concerning Christ to an accompaniment of signs and wonders, particularly healing and deliverance, to such an extent that whole companies of people embraced the gospel. Essential to a recovery of apostolic ministry is the recovery of this supernatural dimension and this is the burden on the hearts of many believers today who are repenting of having ministered a merely cerebral message in the past.

Of equal importance is the realization that the gospel must come in a social context. Preaching has to relate to the actual needs of the people—and that means the church must involve itself in practical caring ministry. The gospel wrapped in a sandwich. In many parts of the world food and medicine are the particular needs. In Britain, social deprivation, personal alienation and cultural confusion are the most likely needs to be met. People—the poor who feel they have no voice; the weak; the elderly; the sick; those who are lonely, distressed, bitter, hurt, perhaps from broken homes; those confused, swamped, trapped by this godless society—these all need, not a tract, but a person who will become involved in their lives.

'God bring us to the day when we are preaching the good news to people with whom we're practically involved whilst the Spirit performs miracles before our eyes,'declared Mr Christian with passion.

'Amen,' agreed his wife.

The Pilgrim Watcher's eyes betrayed his suffused excitement. 'What key to this do you perceive?' he asked.

'I believe the answer lies in appreciating the true nature of the situation and tackling it accordingly,' said Mr Christian.

The others looked to him for an explanation.

'Paul tells us in both Ephesians 6 and 2 Corinthians 10 that our battle is not against flesh and blood but against spiritual forces of wickedness. There's a real enemy invisibly at work behind the outward evil—the devil and his hosts. The reconciliation of all things involves us in spiritual warfare. It isn't simply a matter of preaching the gospel to change the minds of men. Paul says, "The god of this world has blinded the minds of the unbelievers, to keep them from seeing the light of the gospel of the glory of Christ, who is the likeness of God" (2 Corinthians 4:4). Unless, we take the weapons of prayer and the word and deal with the spirits that bind individuals, and indeed the society at large, men and women will not be saved.'

He went on to say how people dwell in darkness and confusion today. Christianity is distorted in their minds, sometimes by those who hold the name of Christ in falsehood. Sects and cults abound, false Christs flourish. Novel paths to wholeness present themselves before the lost. The Aquarian alternative seems attractive. Why is all this? The Scriptures plainly answer, 'The whole world is in the power of the evil one' (1 John 5:19). That power has to be broken if people are to receive the truth which sets them free.

It is not an equal battle. Jesus came in the weakness of human flesh and humbled himself to death on a cross, yet, in that moment of weakness the very power of God was at work. "Since therefore the children share in flesh and blood, he himself likewise partook of the same nature, that through death he might destroy him who has the power of death, that is, the devil, and deliver all those who through fear of death were subject to lifelong bondage" (Hebrews 2:14–15).

'The devil is defeated decisively but it is through the church in each generation that the victory is implemented.' Mr Christian addressed the Courier. 'You were worried this morning about wholeness being a vain ego-trip, Dai. Here, I believe, is your answer. God wants you fighting fit so you will take your place in the army of the Lord and do your part in destroying the kingdom of darkness and establishing the rule of God.'

'That's a tremendous challenge,' the Courier responded solemnly. 'I feel greatly privileged to be called to serve the Lord like this.'

'I, too,' assented Susan. She smiled. 'You know, this is truly the healthy alternative!'

The others laughed.

The Pilgrim Watcher carefully folded his writing implements. The result of all his labours was a large scroll which he concealed under his cloak. He stood and the others did likewise. Solemnly he shook each of their hands and bade them farewell.

For a moment, the company expected him simply to dematerialize but he pointed behind them. They turned to see a coach and horses which had soundlessly appeared. No rider was to be seen. With a smile he strode towards it and entered the vehicle.

'Farewell, my friends, children of the Firstborn. The Lord Almighty be with you and fulfil his purposes in you.'

'Goodbye,' they cried in unison.

The Pilgrim Watcher waved his hand and with no more sound than a rush of wind the coach lifted from the ground to climb in a long slow circle until it was but a speck which soon vanished beyond sight into the gathering cloud.

For a long time the four companions stood in awed silence.

*   *   *

The Pilgrim Watcher looked down upon those four believers as he rose from the earth. As he did, his vision clouded and he saw the scene change.

He stood upon a mountain top. Low, rolling clouds hung over the bleak land below. By a divine impulse, he stretched forth his hand. 'Bring blessing, O Most High,' he cried. A flurry of golden rain, fiery rods like sparks, answered his cry and fell from the clouds. And wherever they struck the earth the colours glowed with light. Again they fell, and again, until the whole land was ablaze with joyous hues.

His vision changed once more and he saw his four companions in the shadowlight of early dawn. Now they stood in a field, prepared for battle. Two armies appeared in opposing ranks. At the one end a disorganized rabble in drab clothing, arguing amongst themselves, sought furiously to drive sad-faced men, women and children to war. At times these people, mercilessly pressed upon by the drab spectral host, would attack one another out of madness and many would fall to rise no more. He felt the anguished cries and endless tears of that bitterly enslaved army. Behind them and their tormentors stood a gaunt black fortress.

His gaze flashed to the other end where his companions had been standing and he saw them now mounted upon horseback amidst a vast army arrayed rank upon rank, waiting, anticipating. Creation held its breath.

Then came forth One upon a white charger, glorious, splendid and majestic. He was the Lord of Hosts. He took his place at the head and there arose a great shout of praise from the assembled host. That very moment the sun broke above the horizon and a thousand shining banners flashed in its light, terrible to behold. The Captain raised his sword and spoke a mighty word. At once, the skies were rent and countless angelic hosts blazed forth to war.

Yet it was not the pitiful humans they attacked but the dark creatures who controlled them from behind. The shout of praise from the shining army resounded across the plain as demons screamed and fled before the onslaught. Dark towers crumbled, ramparts crashed to the ground. Smoke and fire consumed the black fortress until it was no more. And the gates of hell were broken.

Then he beheld an astonishing sight. The former captives of the drab host began to run towards the One upon the horse. Before him they fell, yet, receiving the touch of his sword, arose, miraculously clad in new garments. Then each took his place in the assembled army to be greeted with loving arms by those about him. Their once sad faces now smiled with health, eyes danced with joy, hearts swelled in gratitude.

The vision faded.

'I must hasten to the Council,' determined the Pilgrim Watcher. 'Surely the time is at hand.'

At that moment, it began to rain.

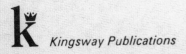

God Wants You Whole
The Way to Healing, Health and Wholeness

by Selwyn Hughes

If God is always willing to heal, why do people remain ill—even when they have faith for healing?

How can we all live more healthy lives, day by day?

With openness and honesty, Selwyn Hughes faces squarely the issues of health and healing that concern every one of us. He examines the most common causes of ill health and the reasons we fail to receive God's healing grace. Here we see how our Creator has lovingly provided all we need for wholeness of living, if only we set ourselves to live in accordance with his will.

Above all, this book shows that even when healing eludes us and our condition is not remedied quickly, we can still rest secure in the knowledge that our heavenly Father is committed to our good—in spirit, mind, emotions, and body.

Also by Selwyn Hughes in Kingsway paperback:
A friend in Need; How to Live the Christian Life; The Christian Counsellor's Pocket Guide; Everyday Reflections; A New Heart; Marriage as God Intended.

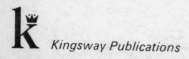

Kingsway Publications

Faith to Live By

by Derek Prince

For the Christian, faith is more than belief: it is an obedient heart that leads to action.

This book shows what biblical faith is, and how it can revolutionize our lives as we claim its promises and its power.

Derek Prince is widely respected in Britain and America for his scholarly yet practical Bible teaching ministry.

Also by Derek Prince in Kingsway paperback: *The Last Word on the Middle East* and, with Lydia Prince, *Appointment in Jerusalem*.

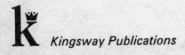

Kingsway Publications

The Father Heart of God

by Floyd McClung

What is God like?

Has he got time for twentieth-century men and women?

Does he really care?

In his work with *Youth with a Mission*, Floyd McClung has met many who suffer from deep emotional hurts and fears.

Time and again it has been the discovery of God as Father—perfect and reliable, unlike any human parent—that has brought healing and liberty.

This book is for you...

...if you find it hard to accept God as a loving father, or
...if you know God's love but would like to share his blessing with others more effectively.

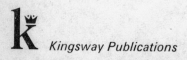

Kingsway Publications